D1233521

Lattices to Logic

,5-49

A BLAISDELL SCIENTIFIC PAPERBACK

Robert E. K. Rourke
SAINT STEPHEN'S SCHOOL, ROME

Consulting Editor

Lattices to Logic

Roy Dubisch

UNIVERSITY OF WASHINGTON

BLAISDELL PUBLISHING COMPANY

NEW YORK TORONTO LONDON

A Division of Ginn and Company

120 10

Copyright © 1964, by Blaisdell Publishing Company,
A Division of Ginn and Company.

LIBRARY OF CONGRESS CATALOG CARD NUMBER: 64-15977

Preface

One of the most striking features of the mathematics of the twentieth century is its unity amidst diversity. Many entirely new branches of mathematics have been developed in the last few years and the older branches have sent forth many vigorous shoots. At the same time there has been a unification of mathematics in that many different-looking branches of mathematics have turned out to have a common root. Furthermore, many seemingly completely abstract and theoretical aspects of mathematics have turned out to be of great usefulness in our increasingly complex modern society.

This book attempts to illustrate this process of unification and application centered around the mathematical concept of a lattice.

No previous background in mathematics is needed for the study of this material except for one short section in which a small amount of first-year high school algebra is used.

In addition to the many examples provided in the text, there are sets of exercises with which the reader may test his understanding of what he has read. Completely worked-out answers to these exercises are included at the end of the book.

ROY DUBISCH

UNIVERSITY OF WASHINGTON

October, 1963

Contents

Lattices	1
Joins and intersections	20
Counting	29
The algebra of sets	35
The algebra of switches	38
Convex sets	48
The algebra of logic	51
History and suggestions for further reading	60
Answers to exercises	62

Lattices

What do a lecturer on painting, a short-order cook, and an arithmetic student have in common?

Consider first the lecturer who wants to make a color diagram to show how the primary colors, yellow, blue, and red, are related to the colors green, orange, and purple. He might draw the diagram shown in Figure 1. Here the point representing green (*g*) is joined to the points

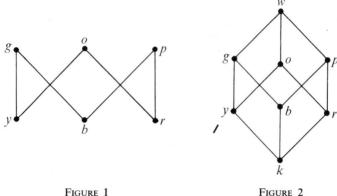

FIGURE 1   FIGURE 2

representing yellow (*y*) and blue (*b*) below it to indicate that green is a mixture of yellow and blue. Similarly, *o* is connected to *y* and *r* below it to indicate that orange is a mixture of yellow and red, and *p* to *b* and *r* to indicate that purple is a mixture of blue and red.

If we regard white (*w*) as a mixture of all colors (as white light can be broken up by a prism into all of the colors of a rainbow) and *k* as the absence of any color, we can extend our diagram to look like Figure 2. Now our diagram shows that white contains green, orange, and purple, as indicated by the line segments joining *w* to *g*, *o*, and *p* below *w*. Furthermore, white also contains yellow since white contains green, and green, in turn, contains yellow. Now

1

to say that yellow, blue, and red contain k (the absence of color) may not appear reasonable. But if we think of k as being a colorless liquid into which pigments are being stirred to make paint, we see that yellow paint does contain k. In any event, we will agree that yellow does contain k so that green, which contains yellow, also contains k; and white, which contains green, also contains k.

It will be easier to analyze such diagrams if we adopt a little notation. We will write, for example, $g \supseteq y$ to indicate that green contains yellow and $g \not\supseteq o$ to indicate that green does not contain orange. In our notation the facts that white contains green, green contains yellow, yellow contains k, and green does not contain red are symbolized by

$$w \supseteq g, \qquad g \supseteq y, \qquad y \supseteq k, \quad \text{and} \quad g \not\supseteq r,$$

respectively. Note that we have, from $w \supseteq g$ and $g \supseteq y$, the result that $w \supseteq y$ and then, from $y \supseteq k$, the result that $w \supseteq k$. This chain-like process is called the *transitive property*: For any colors A, B, and C,

$$\text{if} \quad A \supseteq B \quad \text{and} \quad B \supseteq C, \quad \text{then} \quad A \supseteq C.$$

We will also make the reasonable agreement that, for example, yellow contains yellow and write, in general,

$$A \supseteq A.$$

This property is called the *reflexive property*.

Now if we take any two distinct colors A and B such that $A \supseteq B$, we certainly do not have $B \supseteq A$. For example, $g \supseteq b$ but $b \not\supseteq g$. In general,

$$\text{if} \quad A \supseteq B, \quad \text{then} \quad B \not\supseteq A \quad \text{unless} \quad A = B.$$

This property is called the *antisymmetric property*.

If we want to indicate that $A \supseteq B$ but $A \neq B$ we write $A \supset B$. Thus $w \supset g$, $w \supseteq w$, but $w \not\supset w$.

EXERCISE 1

Determine whether the following statements are true or false. Check by reference to Figure 2.

1. $o \supseteq y$ 6. $w \supset b$
2. $o \supseteq b$ 7. $b \supseteq y$
3. $o \supseteq k$ 8. $b \not\supseteq g$
4. $g \not\supseteq p$ 9. $g \supseteq g$
5. $p \not\supseteq g$ 10. $g \supset g$

* * *

Having laid some groundwork of concepts and notations, let us turn next to the assistance of a short-order cook in a not-too-elegant restaurant at breakfast time. The orders are limited to coffee, oatmeal, and hotcakes. All three may be ordered, any two, or any one. Is it possible for the cook to diagram all possible orders? Let c stand for coffee, o for oatmeal, and h for hotcakes and consider the diagram shown in Figure 3. Here $\{c, o\} \supseteq \{c\}$, $\{c, h\} \supseteq \{c\}$, $\{c\} \supseteq \{c\}$,

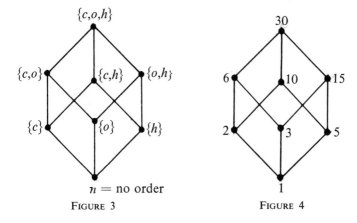

$n = $ no order
FIGURE 3   FIGURE 4

$\{c, o, h\} \supseteq \{c\}$, $\{c, h\} \not\supseteq \{o, h\}$, $\{o, h\} \not\supseteq \{c\}$, and so forth, as indicated by the diagram. Note that, at the very bottom of Figure 3, we have listed the "no order" of the dead beat who comes in only to get warm. We have $\{c\} \supseteq n$, $\{c, o, h\} \supseteq n$, and so forth in the same idealized sense as we used k in the color diagram.

Next let us consider the arithmetic student who has the eight numbers 1, 2, 3, 5, 6, 10, 15, and 30. He observes that all of the numbers listed are divisors of 30, only 1 divides 1, 2 divides 6, 2 does not divide 3, and so forth. To indicate all of this he produces the diagram shown in Figure 4. Now by $30 \supseteq 6$ we mean that 6 divides 30; $2 \supseteq 2$, $6 \supseteq 2$, and $30 \supseteq 2$ mean that 2 divides 2, 2 divides 6, and 2 divides 30, respectively. On the other hand $15 \not\supseteq 2$, $2 \not\supseteq 15$, and $1 \not\supseteq 6$ indicate, respectively, that 2 does not divide 15, 15 does not divide 2, and 6 does not divide 1.

EXERCISE 2

1. Determine whether the following statements are true or false. Check by reference to Figure 3.

    (a) $\{c, o, h\} \not\supseteq \{h\}$ (e) $\{c, h\} \supseteq \{c, h\}$
    (b) $\{c, o\} \not\supseteq \{o, h\}$ (f) $\{c\} \supseteq \{h\}$
    (c) $\{o, h\} \not\supseteq \{c, o\}$ (g) $\{c, o\} \supseteq \{c\}$
    (d) $\{c, o\} \supseteq n$ (h) $\{c\} \not\supseteq \{c, o\}$

2. Determine whether the following statements are true or false. Check by reference to Figure 4.

    (a) $1 \not\supseteq 6$ (e) $10 \supseteq 3$
    (b) $6 \supseteq 1$ (f) $10 \not\supseteq 2$
    (c) $6 \supseteq 15$ (g) $10 \supseteq 1$
    (d) $15 \supseteq 6$ (h) $10 \supseteq 15$

3. Suppose that the restaurant becomes somewhat more elegant, adds eggs (e) to the menu, and gets rid of the dead beats by demanding that all orders must include coffee and everyone must order something. Make a diagram showing all possible orders.

4. Suppose that our arithmetic student has only the numbers 1, 2, 3, 5, 6, 15, and 30 and wishes to produce a "division diagram" similar to Figure 4. What would it look like?

*   *   *

We have seen that the lecturer, the short-order cook, and the arithmetic student do have something in common—a diagram that is (except for labeling) the same for all three. It is one of the functions of the mathematician to note similarities like these between seemingly unrelated phenomena and to ask whether or not a common theory or point of view can be developed to cover all of them. It is a part of this theory and some of its applications that will be presented here.

We want, then, to consider other sets of things and other interpretations of $\supseteq$. For all of these sets and interpretations of $\supseteq$ we can construct a diagram similar to the one just considered in which the points in the diagram correspond to the items in our collection. Furthermore, if A and B are two elements of our set, $A \supseteq B$ if and only if $A = B$ or if we can go from the point corresponding to A to the point corresponding to B by moving always downward on a series of line segments.

Now in any one of our examples we noted that, for all A, B, C in the system we had

(1) $A \supseteq A$ (the reflexive property)

(2) if $A \supseteq B$ and $B \supseteq A$, then $A = B$

                                   (the antisymmetric property)

(3) if $A \supseteq B$ and $B \supseteq C$, then $A \supseteq C$

                                   (the transitive property).

A set with a relation $\supseteq$ defined between elements of the set is called a *partially ordered system.**

Furthermore, we may note that, given any two elements A and B in our examples, there exists at least one element C such that $C \supseteq A$ and $C \supseteq B$. Thus in our first example if we take y as A and b as B, we may take C as g since $g \supseteq y$ and also $g \supseteq b$. But we could also take C as w since $w \supseteq y$ and $w \supseteq b$. On the other hand, we could not, for example, take C as p since while $p \supseteq b$, we have $p \nsupseteq y$. Any C such that $C \supseteq A$ and $C \supseteq B$ is called an *upper bound* for A and B. Thus, in our color example, g and w are upper bounds for y and b and are, in fact, the only upper bounds for y and b.

Now among all of the choices for upper bounds we note in our examples that we have a "least" one (or "lowest" one in terms of a diagram). For y and b this is g and not w since $w \supseteq g$ (or, geometrically, the point corresponding to w in our diagram is above the point corresponding to g). We write $g = y \cup b$ and call g the *least* upper bound of y and b.

As another example, consider k and r. The upper bounds for k and r are

$$r, \ o, \ p, \text{ and } w$$

---

* The word "partially" is used to indicate that, given any two elements A and B, it is possible to have neither $A \supseteq B$ nor $B \supseteq A$. Thus in our first example (Figure 2) we have neither $y \supseteq b$ nor $b \supseteq y$. If, always, for any two elements A and B either $A \supseteq B$ or $B \supseteq A$ and the three properties given above hold, we call the system an *ordered system.*

since $r \supseteq k$, $r \supseteq r$; $o \supseteq k$, $o \supseteq r$; $p \supseteq k$, $p \supseteq r$; $w \supseteq k$, $w \supseteq r$. However, $o \supseteq r$, $p \supseteq r$, and $w \supseteq r$ so that r is the least upper bound: $k \cup r = r$.

As a final example, consider g and w . Here the only upper bound for g and w is w and hence $g \cup w = w$.

Formalizing our notion of "least" we say that $L = A \cup B$, or that L is the least upper bound of A and B if

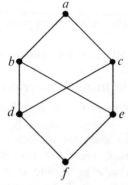

(1) L is an upper bound of A and B (that is, $L \supseteq A$ and $L \supseteq B$) and

(2) if D is any upper bound of A and B , then $D \supseteq L$.

In contrast to the example we have been studying, consider the system with the six elements a , b , c , d , e , and f as diagrammed in Figure 5. (Note that the intersection of the line segment joining b and e with the line segment joining c and d is *not* a point of our diagram.) Then b , c , and a are all of the upper bounds for d and e but none of them is a least upper bound. For, clearly, a is not a

FIGURE 5

least upper bound since b is an upper bound and yet we do not have $b \supseteq a$ as required by (2). But also, b is not a least upper bound since $c \nsupseteq b$ and c is not a least upper bound since $b \nsupseteq c$. Thus $d \cup e$ does not exist. Roughly speaking, b and c are both equally likely candidates for $d \cup e$. But since neither one is below and connected to the other in our diagram, neither one is a *least* upper bound.

This last remark brings up one other point. Is it possible for two elements of a partially ordered system to have two least upper bounds? From the point of view of our diagrams it is obvious that this cannot happen since if $L = A \cup B$ and also $L' = A \cup B$ it would follow that L is below L' and, also, L' is below L . More formally, we note that L and L' are both upper bounds of A and B by (1); then, by (2), if $L = A \cup B$ we have $L' \supseteq L$. But if $L' = A \cup B$, (2) gives us $L \supseteq L'$. We then apply the antisymmetric property to conclude that $L' = L$.

Note that if $A \supseteq B$ we have $A \cup B = A$ and, in particular, $A \cup A = A$.

EXERCISE 3

Refer to Figure 2 if necessary and find as many upper bounds as you can for A and B as given. Then find the least upper bound, $A \cup B$.

1. $A = g$, $B = o$	5. $A = g$, $B = w$
2. $A = b$, $B = r$	6. $A = r$, $B = r$
3. $A = o$, $B = r$	7. $A = p$, $B = w$
4. $A = k$, $B = b$	8. $A = k$, $B = k$

* * *

Similarly, in our examples, if we have given any two elements A and B, then there exists at least one element C such that $A \supseteq C$ and $B \supseteq C$. Thus in our first example (Figure 2) if we take g as A and p as B, we may take C as b since $g \supseteq b$ and also $p \supseteq b$. But we could also take C as k since $g \supseteq k$ and $p \supseteq k$. On the other hand, we could not, for example, take C as y since while $g \supseteq y$, we have $p \nsupseteq y$. Any C such that $A \supseteq C$ and $B \supseteq C$ is called a *lower bound* for A and B. Thus in our example, b and k are lower bounds for g and p and are, in fact, the only lower bounds for g and p.

Now among all the choices for lower bounds we note that we have a "greatest" one (or "highest" one in terms of a diagram). For g and p this is b and not k since $b \supseteq k$ (or, geometrically, the point corresponding to k is below the point corresponding to b). We write $b = g \cap p$ and call b the *greatest* lower bound of g and p.

As another example, consider w and o. The lower bounds for w and o are

$$o, y, r, \text{ and } k$$

since $w \supseteq o$, $o \supseteq o$; $w \supseteq y$, $o \supseteq y$; $w \supseteq r$, $o \supseteq r$; $w \supseteq k$, $o \supseteq k$. However, $o \supseteq y$, $o \supseteq r$, and $o \supseteq k$ so that o is the greatest lower bound: $w \cap o = o$.

As a final example, consider b and k. Here the only lower bound for b and k is k and hence $b \cap k = k$.

Formalizing our notion of "greatest" we say that $G = A \cap B$ or that G is the greatest lower bound of A and B if

(1) G is a lower bound of A and B (that is, $A \supseteq G$ and $B \supseteq G$), and

(2) If D is any lower bound of A and B, then $G \supseteq D$.

Now consider the system diagrammed in Figure 5. Here d, e, and f are all of the lower bounds for b and c but none of them is a *greatest* lower bound. For clearly f is not a greatest lower bound since e is also a lower bound and $e \supseteq f$. But, also, d is not a greatest lower bound since $d \not\supseteq e$ and yet e is also a lower bound. Likewise e is not a greatest lower bound since $e \not\supseteq d$ and yet d is also a lower bound. Thus $b \cap c$ does not exist. Roughly speaking, d and e are both equally likely candidates for $b \cap c$. But since neither one is above and connected to the other in our diagram, neither one is a greatest lower bound.

We note that if $A \supseteq B$ we have $A \cap B = B$ and, in particular, that $A \cap A = A$. We leave as an exercise for the reader the proof that two elements A and B never have more than one greatest lower bound.

EXERCISE 4

1. Refer to Figure 2 if necessary and find as many lower bounds as you can for A and B as given. Then find the greatest lower bound, $A \cap B$.

(a)	$A = g, B = o$	(e)	$A = g, B = w$
(b)	$A = b, B = r$	(f)	$A = r, B = r$
(c)	$A = o, B = r$	(g)	$A = p, B = w$
(d)	$A = k, B = b$	(h)	$A = k, B = k$

2. Prove that two elements A and B of a partially ordered system never have more than one greatest lower bound.

* * *

We have seen that our examples involving colors, meal orders, and arithmetic have the following properties for all A, B, and C in the system:

(1) $A \supseteq A$;
(2) if $A \supseteq B$ and $B \supseteq A$, then $A = B$;   }   partially ordered system
(3) if $A \supseteq B$ and $B \supseteq C$, then $A \supseteq C$;
(4) A and B have a (unique) least upper bound, $A \cup B$; and
(5) A and B have a (unique) greatest lower bound, $A \cap B$.

Any system in which we have a relation, $\supseteq$, between elements of the system that satisfies the five requirements listed above is called a *lattice*. A lattice is frequently most conveniently described by a diagram. In Figure 6 some diagrams of lattices are shown. On the other hand, we have seen that the diagram in Figure 5 is not the diagram of a lattice ($b \cap c$ and $d \cup e$ do not exist).

We ask: When is a diagram consisting of points and line segments joining these points the diagram of a lattice?

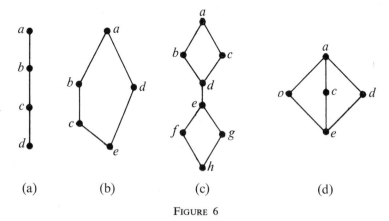

(a)   (b)   (c)   (d)

FIGURE 6

We recall that the geometrical interpretation of $A \supseteq B$ is that either $A = B$ or we can go from the point corresponding to A to the point corresponding to B by moving always downward on a series of line segments. (For convenience we will say that A and B are *connected* to mean that we can go from A to B by always moving downward on a series of line segments or from B to A by always moving downward in a series of line segments.) Thus requirement (1)— $A \supset A$ —is always trivially satisfied in any diagram. Likewise (2)—if $A \supseteq B$ and $B \supseteq A$, then $A = B$ —is always trivially satisfied since it simply asserts that if A and B are two connected points it is not possible to have A both above B and below B . Implicitly, this also says that we have no horizontal line segments in our diagram, since if two points were connected by a horizontal line segment we could not decide which was higher. Thus we list as our first requirement for a diagram to represent a lattice:

(I)   No line segment joining two points is horizontal.

Still further, requirement (3)—if $A \supseteq B$ and $B \supseteq C$, then $A \supseteq C$ —is trivially satisfied since it simply asserts that if we can go from A to B by moving always downward on a series of line segments, and then from B to C by moving always downward on a series of line segments, we can certainly go from A to C by moving always downward (through B) on a series of line segments. (We have supposed that $A \neq B$ and $B \neq C$. If $A = B$ or $B = C$ the situation is even simpler.)

Consider now requirement (4)—existence of least upper bounds. When $A \supseteq B$ we have noted that $A \cup B = A$ and when $B \supseteq A$, $A \cup B = B$. Hence in considering points in our diagram with regard to condition (4), we need only consider pairs A and B such that $A \nsupseteq B$ and $B \nsupseteq A$. Thus (4) may be stated as follows in terms of a diagram:

(II)   Given any two distinct points A and B such that $A \nsupseteq B$ and $B \nsupseteq A$ (that is, A is not above and connected* to B nor is B above and connected to A). Then there exists a point L such that (1) L is above A and B and connected to A and B, and (2) if C is any other point above A and B and connected to A and B, then C is also above L and connected to L.

Thus, for example, in Figure 6 (a), for any two points A and B, we always have $A \supseteq B$ or $B \supseteq A$ so that requirement (II) is trivially satisfied. For Figure 6 (b), the only pairs of points A and B not satisfying the condition $A \supseteq B$ or $B \supseteq A$ are the pairs (b, d) and (c, d). In both cases $L = a$; that is, $b \cup d = c \cup d = a$. In Figure 6 (c) we need only note that $b \cup c = a$ and $f \cup g = e$ and in Figure 6 (d) that $b \cup c = b \cup d = c \cup d = a$.

On the other hand, in Figure 5, the only points above d and e and connected to d and e are b, c, and a. But a cannot be used as the least upper bound since a is also above b and connected to it. Similarly, if b were equal to $d \cup e$ we would have to have c above b and connected to it—contrary to fact. Likewise if c were equal to $d \cup e$ we would have to have b above c and connected to it— again contrary to fact. Thus the diagram of Figure 5 is not the diagram of a lattice.

Similarly, condition (5)—existence of greatest lower bounds—

---

* Recall our definition of "connected" on p. 9.

becomes

(III)   Given any two distinct points A and B such that $B \not\supseteq A$ and $A \not\supseteq B$ (that is, A is not below B and connected to B nor is B below A and connected to A). Then there exists a point G such that (1) G is below A and B and connected to A and B and (2) if C is any other point below A and B and connected to A and B, then C is also below G and connected to G.

Again, for Figure 6 (a), requirement (II) is trivially satisfied. For Figure 6 (b), the only pairs of points not satisfying the condition $A \supseteq B$ or $B \supseteq A$ are the pairs (b, d) and (c, d). In both cases, $G = e$; that is, $b \cap d = c \cap d = e$. In Figure 6 (c), we need only note that $b \cap c = d$ and $f \cap g = h$; in Figure 6 (d) that $b \cap c = b \cap d = c \cap d = e$.

On the other hand, in Figure 5, the only points below b and c and connected to them are d, e, and f. But f cannot be used as the greatest lower bound since d is above f and connected to it. Similarly, if d were equal to $b \cap c$ we would have to have e below d and connected to it—contrary to fact; and if e were equal to $b \cap c$ we would have to have d below e and connected to it—again contrary to fact. Thus we again conclude that the diagram of Figure 5 is not the diagram of a lattice.

We have seen several diagrams (Figures 2 and 6) that do represent lattices and one (Figure 5) that does not. In Figure 7 (p. 13) are other diagrams that do not represent lattices.

In Figure 7 (a) we have a horizontal line, contrary to requirement (I); in (b) $a \cup b$ does not exist, contrary to requirement (II), since there is no point above a and b ; in (c) $b \cup c$ does not exist, contrary to requirement (II), since we have no point above *and connected* to c ; in (d) $c \cap d$ does not exist, contrary to requirement (III), since we have no point below and connected to d ; in (e), for any two points A and B such that $A \not\supseteq B$ and $B \not\supseteq A$, we do have at least one point above and connected to A and B as well as at least one point below and connected to A and B. That is, the first part of requirements (II) and (III) is satisfied. But, for example, $e \cup f$ does not exist since b, c, and d are above and connected to e and f and yet none of these are above and connected to each other (d is above both b and c but *not* connected to either b or c). Similarly, $b \cap c$, $b \cap d$, and $c \cap d$ do not exist. Thus the second part is not satisfied in either condition (II) or condition (III).

EXERCISE 5

1. In Figure 6 (a) find $b \cup d$, $c \cup a$, $b \cap d$, and $c \cap a$.
2. In Figure 6 (b) find $a \cup c$, $d \cup e$, $a \cap c$, and $d \cap e$.
3. In Figure 6 (c) find $b \cup e$, $f \cup g$, $b \cap e$, and $f \cap g$.
4. In Figure 6 (d) find $b \cup a$, $c \cup d$, $b \cap a$, and $c \cap d$.
5. Which of the following diagrams represent lattices and which do not?

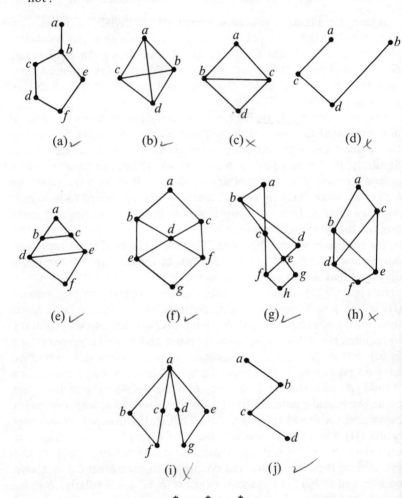

(a) ✓   (b) ✓   (c) ✗   (d) ✗

(e) ✓   (f) ✓   (g) ✓   (h) ✗

(i) ✗   (j) ✓

*   *   *

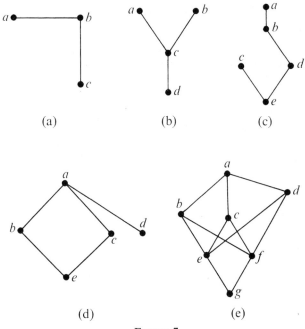

FIGURE 7

A diagram of a lattice is not the lattice and a lattice may be pictured by many different diagrams. For example, the lattice whose diagram is labeled (b) in Figure 6 may be diagrammed in many ways including those shown in Figure 8. Here (a) is the original diagram; in (a)′ we note

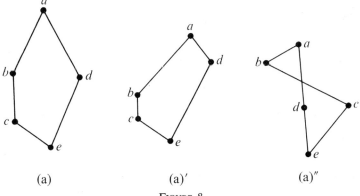

FIGURE 8

that the position of *d* has been shifted relative to *e* but since *b* and *d* are not connected, this is of no consequence. That is, in (a) we have $b \nsupseteq d$ and $d \nsupseteq b$ and this is still true in (a)'. In (a)" we observe that we have some crossing line segments which do not, however, alter our relations $b \supseteq c$, $a \supseteq c$, $c \supseteq e$, $b \nsupseteq d$, $d \nsupseteq b$, and so forth.

On the other hand, the two diagrams shown in Figure 9 are *not* diagrams of the lattice diagrammed in Figure 6 (b). For, in the left-hand diagram we have $d \supseteq a$ instead of $a \supseteq d$, and $d \supseteq b$ instead of $d \nsupseteq b$, and so forth. In the right-hand diagram we have $e \supseteq c$ instead of $c \supseteq e$, $b \nsupseteq e$ instead of $b \supseteq e$, and so on.

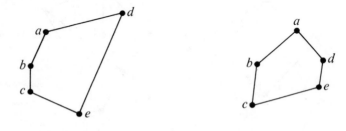

FIGURE 9

EXERCISE 6

1. Which of the following diagrams represent the same lattice as the one labeled (a) in Figure 6?

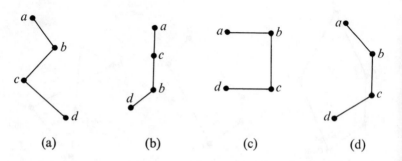

(a)   (b)   (c)   (d)

2. Which of the following diagrams represent the same lattice as the one labeled (d) in Figure 6?

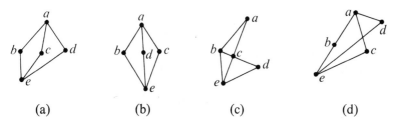

(a)   (b)   (c)   (d)

3. Draw a "simpler" diagram for the lattice labeled (b) in problem 5 of Exercise 5 (that is, a diagram with fewer line segments). Do likewise for the lattice labeled (e).

*   *   *

Let us return now to our question of when a diagram is a diagram of a lattice. It is indeed easy to see when condition (I) (no horizontal line segments) is satisfied and just about as easy to see when the first parts of conditions (II) and (III)—existence of upper bounds and lower bounds—is satisfied (if it isn't, the diagram is obviously "incomplete"— one point, at least, besides the point at the very bottom and the point at the very top is left unconnected above or below). What we wish to show now is that if there are no horizontal lines, if every two elements have at least one upper bound and at least one lower bound, and if there are no intersecting lines in the diagram that are not labeled as points [that is, no intersections such as be and dc in Figure 5 or bf and ec in Figure 7 (e)], then the diagram represents a lattice.

Suppose, then, that we have a diagram in which there are no horizontal line segments, in which every two elements have at least one upper bound and at least one lower bound, and in which there are no line segments intersecting at points other than those of our diagram. We wish to show that every two points do have a least upper bound and a greatest lower bound so that the diagram does represent a lattice.

Now for two points A and B with $A \supseteq B$ we have $A \cup B = A$ and $A \cap B = B$ so we need only consider points A and B such that $A \not\supseteq B$ and $B \not\supseteq A$. Now A and B have at least one upper bound by hypothesis; if A and B have only one upper bound it is, of course, a least upper bound. Now suppose that A and B have more than one upper bound; they can be listed as C, D, E, F, ... If X and Y are any two distinct points in this list such that $X \supseteq Y$ we discard X from this list (such an X clearly could not be a *least* upper bound).

At least one point will remain after this process since if $X \supseteq Y$ we cannot have $Y \supseteq X$ unless $X = Y$ (antisymmetric property).

If only one point remains in this reduced list we have already observed that we then have a least upper bound. Now suppose that we have at

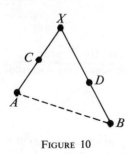

FIGURE 10

least two upper bounds, X and Y, in this reduced list where $X \not\supseteq Y$ and $Y \not\supseteq X$. We consider the portion of our diagram involving X, A, and B as shown in Figure 10. (The diagram may, of course, be much more complicated than the one shown here. But the analysis to be described will not be affected by a greater complexity of the diagram.) We complete the polygon (here, a triangle) by the dotted line segment joining A to B.

Now if Y is another upper bound such that $X \not\supseteq Y$ and $Y \not\supseteq X$ we know that there is an upper bound Z for X and Y with $Z \neq X$ and $Z \neq Y$ as shown in Figure 11 for the case where Y lies outside of our polygon. Since Y is an upper bound for A and B it must be connected to both A and B. We want to show that this implies that some line segment intersects another line segment at other than a point of our diagram. Consider the connection from A to Y and remember that the line segments used must always go upward. This means that the connection from A to Y must cross the line segments joining B to X or the line segments joining X to Z. If it is to cross only at a point of our diagram we have the two possibilities as shown in Figure 12. (The case when Y is not above X is even simpler since it involves only the first possibility; the case when

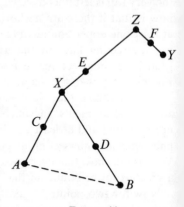

FIGURE 11

Y is to the left of the polygon is handled by considering the connection from B to Y. Also, if such points as D and E do not exist on the line segments joining B to X and X to Z we simply conclude directly that connections cannot be made from A to Y). In case (a), however, D would then be an upper bound of A and B

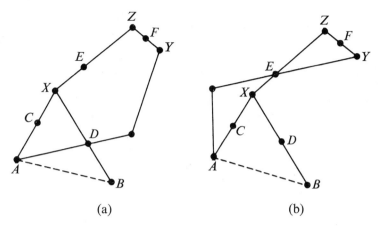

(a)   (b)

FIGURE 12

with $X \supseteq D$, contrary to our construction of the set of upper bounds of which X is a member. In case (b) we would have $Y \supseteq X$, again contrary to fact.

On the other hand, if Y were in the interior of the polygon we would first note that Y cannot be above the points (if any) lying on the line segments joining A to X and B to Y (as shown in Figure 13). For if this were the case we could not construct the necessary upper bound, Z, for X and Y without having the line segments joining Y to Z intersect the line segments joining B to X or A to

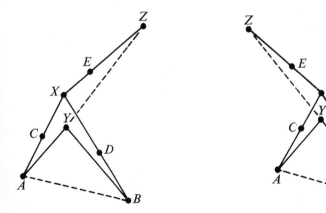

FIGURE 13

X at other than a point of our diagram. Now suppose Y is below the points on the line segments joining A to X and B to X as shown in Figure 14. Join A and B to Y and Y to Z by line segments as in Figure 14 (a) or Figure 14 (b). (Y must be above A and B and connected to A and B since we are assuming that Y is an upper bound for A and B.) Then D and C, respectively, become upper bounds for A and B with $X \supseteq D$ or $X \supseteq C$ —again a contradiction.

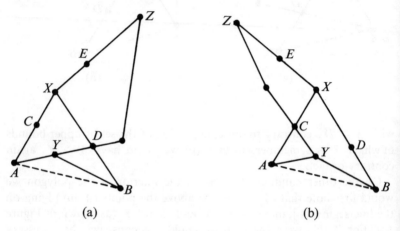

(a)   (b)

FIGURE 14

The case when Y is below the points on one set of line segments (say, below C) and above the other set (say, above D) is handled similarly. Finally we observe that if points such as C and D do not exist, we cannot have Y in the interior and that Y certainly cannot lie on the line segments joining A to X or B to X.

The case of the greatest lower bound may be treated similarly and is left as an exercise for the reader.

The reader should be sure that he understands both the strengths and the limitations of the result just obtained. On the one hand, it tells us that if we look at a diagram and see that

(1)   It has no horizontal line segments;
(2)   It is "complete" (no points are unconnected to other points above and below except for the two top and bottom points);
(3)   It has no line segments intersecting at other than the points of the diagram,

then our diagram is the diagram of a lattice. Thus the diagrams in Figure 6 are immediately seen to be diagrams of lattices **by** using these criteria.

On the other hand, just because there are intersecting line segments that are not points of the diagrams it does *not* follow that our diagram is not a lattice diagram. Thus our first example (Figure 2) involves such intersecting line segments and, yet, of course, it is the diagram of a lattice. (And it should be clear that no possible diagram of this lattice can be made without some such intersecting line segments.)

EXERCISE 7

Use the criteria just established, when applicable, to determine whether the diagrams of Figure 6 and of problem 5 of Exercise 5 represent lattices.

*   *   *

Now, although we are at perfect liberty to draw a lattice without any specific idea in mind as to what it might represent, it is true that the lattices in Figure 6 do have simple interpretations.* For the lattice labeled (a) let us consider a, b, c, and d to be the numbers 5, 4, 3, and 2, respectively, and by $A \supseteq B$ to mean that the number A is greater than or equal to the number B. Thus $5 \supseteq 5$, $5 \supseteq 2$, $3 \supseteq 2$, $2 \not\supseteq 4$, and so on. Notice that, in this case, for any two distinct elements A and B we have either $A \supseteq B$ or $B \supseteq A$. This was not true in the lattice of colors where, for example $g \not\supseteq o$ and also $o \not\supseteq g$.

For our lattice labeled (b) we can take $a = 30$, $b = 15$, $c = 5$, $d = 6$, and $e = 1$ and interpret $A \supseteq B$ to mean that A is divisible by B. Thus $a \supseteq a$, $a \supseteq b$, $a \supseteq c$, $a \supseteq d$, and $a \supseteq e$ since 30 is divisible by 30, 15, 5, 6, and 1. Similarly, $b \supseteq c$, $b \not\supseteq d$, $d \not\supseteq b$, and so forth.

For our lattice labeled (c) we have the interpretation

$$a = \{1, 2, 3, 4, 5, 6\}$$

(the set consisting of the numbers 1, 2, 3, 4, 5, and 6),

$$b = \{1, 2, 3, 4, 5\}, \quad c = \{1, 2, 3, 5, 6\}, \quad d = \{1, 2, 3, 5\},$$
$$e = \{1, 2, 3\}, \qquad f = \{1, 2\}, \qquad g = \{1, 3\},$$

* Of course, interpretations are not unique as our first example of lecturer-cook-student showed.

and
$$h = \{1\}.$$

Here $A \supseteq B$ means that every element of B is an element of A. Thus $a \supseteq a$, $a \supseteq e$, $a \supseteq b$, $b \supseteq e$, $b \supseteq f$, $c \supseteq c$, $f \nsupseteq b$, $b \nsupseteq c$, $c \nsupseteq b$, and so forth. Notice, by the way, that this lattice can also be represented by the diagram shown in Figure 15. Here the line segments

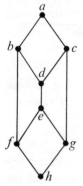

FIGURE 15

bf and cg have been added but tell us nothing new. We already had, for example, $b \supseteq f$ and $c \supseteq g$.

Finally, consider the lattice labeled (d). For our interpretation consider a spy ring consisting of spies with the code names a, b, c, d, and e. We suppose that a is the chief of the ring and, as such, knows not only his own real name but the real names of b, c, d, and e. On the other hand, b knows only his own real name and e's real name; c knows only his own real name and e's real name; and d knows only his own real name and e's real name. Finally, e, new to the organization, knows only his own real name. Our interpretation of $A \supseteq B$, of course, is that A knows B's real name. Thus $a \supseteq a$, $a \supseteq b$, $a \supseteq c$, $a \supseteq d$, $a \supseteq e$, $b \supseteq e$, $e \nsupseteq b$, $b \nsupseteq c$, $c \nsupseteq b$, and so forth.

EXERCISE 8

Give an interpretation of each of the lattices labeled (a), (b), and (e) in problem 5 of Exercise 5.

*   *   *

Joins and Intersections

We have seen that lattices can be used to represent various relationships. More is possible. We have already described a method o combining any two points of a lattice to obtain a third point. The combination $A \cup B$ is often called the *join* (or *union*) of A and B rather than the least upper bound.

To illustrate further the concept of the join of two points, Table 1 is a complete "join table" for our first example (Figure 2). This table is

Table 1.

$\cup$	w	g	o	p	y	b	r	k
w	w	w	w	w	w	w	w	w
g	w	g	w	w	g	g	w	g
o	w	w	o	w	o	w	o	o
p	w	w	w	p	w	p	p	p
y	w	g	o	w	y	g	o	y
b	w	g	w	p	g	b	p	b
r	w	w	o	p	o	p	r	r
k	w	g	o	p	y	b	r	k

read just as an ordinary addition or multiplication table for numbers. Thus to find $y \cup b$ we locate y in the extreme left-hand column and then follow across horizontally until we come to the column headed b on the top line. The entry, g, found there is the least upper bound of y and b: $y \cup b = g$. Similarly, $p \cup b = p$, $r \cup r = r$, $o \cup p = w$, and so forth.

From our table for our example and from the definition in general we see that, for any two points x and y we have

$$x \cup y = y \cup x$$

and

$$x \cup x = x.$$

We may also notice that, for the "top" point, w, in our lattice we have

$$w \cup x = x \cup w = w$$

for any point x; for the "bottom" point, k, we have

$$k \cup x = x \cup k = x$$

for any point x.

There are some obvious similarities between the join operation for a lattice and the addition operation for numbers. Thus $x \cup y = y \cup x$

for our lattice and $x + y = y + x$ for numbers; $k \cup x = x \cup k = x$
for our lattice and $0 + x = x + 0 = x$ for numbers. On the other
hand, there are some striking differences: $x \cup x = x$ for all points x,
but $x + x = x$ for numbers only if $x = 0$. We will explore these
similarities and differences later.

EXERCISE 9

Construct join tables for:
1. The lattice labeled (a) in Figure 6.
2. The lattice labeled (b) in Figure 6.
3. The lattice labeled (c) in Figure 6.
4. The lattice labeled (d) in Figure 6.
5. The lattice labeled (a) in problem 5 of Exercise 5.
6. The lattice labeled (e) in problem 5 of Exercise 5 (use the results of
   problem 3 of Exercise 6).

*   *   *

The combination $A \cap B$ for lattice elements is often called the
intersection (or *meet*) of A and B rather than the greatest lower
bound of A and B.

As was true for join, our results concerning intersection in our
example are most conveniently summarized in a table (Table 2).

Table 2.

$\cap$	w	g	o	p	y	b	r	k
w	w	g	o	p	y	b	r	k
g	g	g	y	b	y	b	k	k
o	o	y	o	r	y	k	r	k
p	p	b	r	p	k	b	r	k
y	y	y	y	k	y	k	k	k
b	b	b	k	b	k	b	k	k
r	r	k	r	r	k	k	r	k
k	k	k	k	k	k	k	k	k

We note that $x \cap y = y \cap x$, $x \cap x = x$, $w \cap x = x$, and
$k \cap x = x \cap k = k$ for all elements x and y of our lattice.

EXERCISE 10

Construct intersection tables for:
1. The lattice labeled (a) in Figure 6.
2. The lattice labeled (b) in Figure 6.
3. The lattice labeled (c) in Figure 6.
4. The lattice labeled (d) in Figure 6.
5. The lattice labeled (a) in problem 1 of Exercise 5.
6. The lattice labeled (e) in problem 5 of Exercise 5 (use the results of problem 3 of Exercise 6).

*   *   *

We have observed that, for any lattice,

$$A \cup B = B \cup A \quad \text{and} \quad A \cap B = B \cap A$$

(the commutative properties)

and that

$$A \cup A = A \quad \text{and} \quad A \cap A = A$$

(the idempotent properties)

for all elements A and B of the lattice. Furthermore, because of requirement (4) there is a "highest" element U such that

$$U \cap A = A \cap U = A$$

(identity for intersection)

for all elements A of the lattice; and because of requirement (5) there is a "lowest" element Z such that

$$Z \cup A = A \cup Z = A$$

(identity for join)

for all points A of the lattice.

The next properties we give are analogous to the arithmetic properties $(a + b) + c = a + (b + c)$ and $(a \times b) \times c = a \times (b \times c)$.

$$(A \cup B) \cup C = A \cup (B \cup C) \quad \text{and} \quad (A \cap B) \cap C = A \cap (B \cap C).$$

(the associative properties)

For example, in our first illustration (Figure 2) we have

$$(y \cup b) \cup r = g \cup r = w, \qquad y \cup (b \cup r) = y \cup p = w,$$

and

$$(y \cap b) \cap r = k \cap r = k, \qquad y \cap (b \cap r) = y \cap k = k.$$

In general, from a geometrical point of view, $(A \cup B) \cup C$ is the lowest point above and connected to A, B, and C and this is obviously the same point as $A \cup (B \cup C)$ since it doesn't matter whether we first consider A and B and then C or first A and then B and C. A similar line of reasoning establishes that $A \cap (B \cap C) = (A \cap B) \cap C$.

In ordinary arithmetic we have $a \times (b + c) = (a \times b) + (a \times c)$ as in $3 \times (4 + 5) = 3 \times 9 = 27$ and $(3 \times 4) + (3 \times 5) = 12 + 15 = 27$. We do not, however, have $a + (b \times c) = (a + b) \times (a + c)$. Thus $2 + (3 \times 4) = 2 + 12 = 14$ but $(2 + 3) \times (2 + 4) = 5 \times 6 = 30$. In *some* lattices, however, we do have both versions:

$$A \cap (B \cup C) = (A \cap B) \cup (A \cap C)$$

and

$$A \cup (B \cap C) = (A \cup B) \cap (A \cup C)$$

(the *distributive* properties)

and, in fact, it can be shown that if one of these versions of the distributive property holds, then the other one must also. For example, in our first illustration we have

$$y \cap (b \cup r) = y \cap p = k \quad \text{and} \quad (y \cap b) \cup (y \cap r) = k \cup k = k.$$

Also

$$y \cup (b \cap r) = y \cup k = y \quad \text{and} \quad (y \cup b) \cap (y \cup r) = g \cap o = y.$$

However, while lattices possess the commutative, idempotent, and associative properties, not all lattices possess the distributive properties. For example, in the lattice diagram labeled (b) in Figure 6 we have

$$c \cup (d \cap b) = c \cup e = c$$

but

$$(c \cup d) \cap (c \cup b) = a \cap b = b.$$

Similarly, in the lattice diagram labeled (d) in Figure 6 we have

$$c \cup (d \cap b) = c \cup e = c$$

but

$$(c \cup d) \cap (c \cup b) = a \cap a = a.$$

As a matter of fact, it can be shown that the only lattices that do not possess the distributive properties are the two just mentioned and those lattices that contain either one (or both) of these as "parts," as in, for example, the lattice diagrams shown in Figure 16.

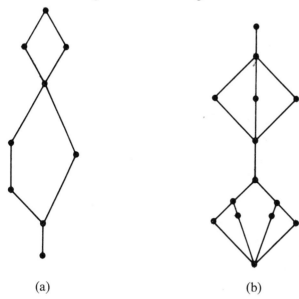

(a)   (b)

FIGURE 16

EXERCISE 11

1. For the lattice labeled (a) in Figure 6 verify that

  (a) $a \cup (b \cup c) = (a \cup b) \cup c$;
  (b) $a \cap (b \cap c) = (a \cap b) \cap c$;
  (c) $a \cup (b \cap c) = (a \cup b) \cap (a \cup c)$;
  (d) $a \cap (b \cup c) = (a \cap b) \cup (a \cap c)$.

. For the lattice labeled (b) in Figure 6 verify that

  (a) $a \cup (b \cup d) = (a \cup b) \cup d$;
  (b) $a \cap (b \cap d) = (a \cap b) \cap d$.

. For the lattice labeled (c) in Figure 6 verify that

  (a) $b \cup (c \cup f) = (b \cup c) \cup f$;
  (b) $b \cap (c \cap f) = (b \cap c) \cap f$;
  (c) $b \cup (c \cap f) = (b \cup c) \cap (b \cup f)$;
  (d) $b \cap (c \cup f) = (b \cap c) \cup (b \cap f)$.

4. For the lattice labeled (d) in Figure 6 verify that

    (a) $a \cup (c \cup d) = (a \cup c) \cup d$;

    (b) $a \cap (c \cap d) = (a \cap c) \cap d$.

5. For the lattice labeled (a) in problem 5 of Exercise 5 verify that

    (a) $a \cup (c \cup e) = (a \cup c) \cup e$;

    (b) $a \cap (c \cap e) = (a \cap c) \cap e$.

6. For the lattice labeled (e) in problem 5 of Exercise 5 verify that

    (a) $c \cup (b \cup d) = (c \cup b) \cup d$;

    (b) $(c \cap b) \cap d = c \cap (b \cap d)$;

    (c) $c \cup (b \cap d) = (c \cup b) \cap (c \cup d)$;

    (d) $c \cap (b \cup d) = (c \cap b) \cup (c \cap d)$.

7. The lattices labeled (b) and (d) in Figure 6 do not, as we have seen, enjoy the distributive properties. That is, it is *not* true that for *all* points A, B, and C of these lattices we have

$$A \cup (B \cap C) = (A \cup B) \cap (A \cup C)$$

and

$$A \cap (B \cup C) = (A \cap B) \cup (A \cap C).$$

Can you, however, find some points A, B, and C for which these statements are true in each of these two lattices?

8. A lattice is called a *modular* lattice if, for all points A, B, and C of the lattice such that $C \supseteq A$, we have

$$A \cup (B \cap C) = (A \cup B) \cap C.$$

Show that the lattice labeled (d) in Figure 6 is a modular lattice but that the lattice labeled (b) is not a modular lattice.

*   *   *

Let us return once more to our first example with a different labeling (Figure 17). We have had three interpretations of this lattice—one involving colors, one involving meal orders, and one involving numbers

Now let us consider a slightly more abstract interpretation very closely related, however, to the meal order one.

Thus we now let $U = \{a, b, c\}$, the set consisting of a, b, and c (without specifying exactly what a, b, and c represent); $A = \{a, b\}$; $B = \{a, c\}$; $C = \{b, c\}$; $D = \{a\}$; $E = \{b\}$; $F = \{c\}$; and $Z =$ the empty or *null* set (often designated by $\varnothing$). We define

(1) $X \supseteq Y$ if and only if every element of Y is an element of X.
($U = \{a, b, c\} \supseteq A = \{a, b\}$, $B = \{a, c\} \supseteq D = \{a\}$, $B \supseteq B$; and
$U \supseteq Z$, $A \supseteq Z$, $B \supseteq Z, \ldots, F \supseteq Z$, $Z \supseteq Z$, and so forth.)

Then

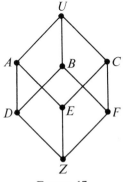

(2) $X \cup Y$ is the set consisting of all the elements that are in either X or Y (or both).
($U \cup A = \{a, b, c\} \cup \{a, b\} = \{a, b, c\} = U$; $A \cup B = \{a, b\} \cup \{a, c\} = \{a, b, c\} = U$; $D \cup E = \{a\} \cup \{b\} = \{a, b\} = A$; $D \cup Z = D$, and so on.)

and

(3) $X \cap Y$ is the set consisting of all the elements that are both in X and in Y.
($U \cap A = \{a, b, c\} \cap \{a, b\} = \{a, b\} = A$; $A \cap B = \{a, b\} \cap \{a, c\} = \{a\} = D$; $D \cap E = \{a\} \cap \{b\} = Z$; $C \cap Z = Z$, and so on.)

FIGURE 17

As before, of course, we could make tables for joins and intersections and they would look exactly like the tables on pages 21 and 22 except for the replacement of w, g, o, p, y, b, r, and k by U, A, B, C, D, E, F, and Z, respectively. All that we are doing here is to provide a shift, in the case when our interpretation is that of sets, from a geometric point of view of $\supseteq$, $\cup$, and $\cap$ to an algebraic one.

If $X \supseteq Y$ we will say that Y is a *subset* of X. In particular, then, X is a subset of X and Z is a subset of every set. Consider now any (finite) set U and a collection of subsets of U : U, A, B, C, ..., $Z = \varnothing$ that includes both U and Z. It should be clear that we can always form a lattice from this collection of subsets by beginning with U at the top and ending with Z at the bottom. A subset A of U is placed above a subset B and connected to B if and only if $A \supseteq B$ and $A \neq B$. Figure 18 shows the lattice corresponding to the following subsets of $U = \{a, b, c, d\}$:

$$U = \{a, b, c, d\}, \qquad\qquad D = \{c, d\},$$
$$A = \{a, c, d\}, \qquad\qquad E = \{c\},$$
$$B = \{b, c, d\}, \qquad\qquad F = \{d\},$$
$$C = \{a, b\}, \qquad\qquad Z = \varnothing.$$

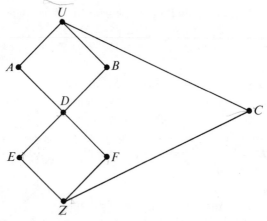

FIGURE 18

EXERCISE 12

1. Consider sets whose elements are a, b, c, d, or e and calculate:

    (a) $\{a, b, c\} \cup \{b, c\}$ (e) $\{a, b\} \cup \{a, b\}$

    (b) $\{a\} \cap \{b, c\}$ (f) $\{c, d\} \cap \{c, d\}$

    (c) $\{b, c\} \cup \{d, e\}$ (g) $\{a, b, c\} \cup \{a, b\}$

    (d) $\{b, c, e\} \cap \{d, e\}$ (h) $\{a, b, c\} \cap \{a, b\}$

2. Prove that, for any sets X and Y, $X \cup Y = X$ if and only if $X \supseteq Y$.

3. Prove that, for any sets X and Y, $X \cap Y = X$ if and only if $Y \supseteq X$.

4. List all of the subsets of the set $U = \{a, b, c, d\}$.

5. How many subsets of a set of n elements are there?

6. Construct a lattice corresponding to the following subsets of $U = \{a, b, c, d\}$: U, $A = \{a, b, c\}$, $B = \{a, b\}$, $C = \{a, c\}$, $D = \{b, c\}$, $E = \{a\}$, $F = \{b\}$, $Z = \varnothing$.

*   *   *

Counting

Let us now do a bit of counting. For every (finite) set A we define $N(A)$ to be the number of elements in the set A. Thus $N(\{a\}) = N(\{b\}) = 1$, $N(\{a, b\}) = N(\{b, c\}) = 2$, $N(\{a, b, c\}) = 3$, $N(\varnothing) = 0$, and so forth.

Suppose now that we want to find $N(A \cup B)$, the number of elements that are in A or in B (or in both). We claim that

$$N(A \cup B) = N(A) + N(B) - N(A \cap B),$$

since, to count the number of elements in $A \cup B$, we may count the number of elements in A $[N(A)]$, add to this the number of elements in B $[N(B)]$, and then subtract from this sum the number of elements we have counted twice because they are in both A and in B $[N(A \cap B)]$. For example, if $A = \{a, b, c\}$ and $B = \{a, b, c\}$, then $A \cup B = \{a, b, c\}$ and $N(A \cup B) = 3$ by direct count. On the other hand, since $A \cap B = \{a, b, c\}$, $N(A \cap B) = 3$ and

$$N(A) + N(B) - N(A \cap B) = 3 + 3 - 3 = 3.$$

As another example, consider $A = \{a, b, d\}$ and $B = \{a, c\}$. Then $A \cup B = \{a, b, c, d\}$ and $N(A \cup B) = 4$. But now $N(A) = 3$, $N(B) = 2$, and, since $A \cap B = \{a\}$, $N(A \cap B) = 1$. Thus

$$N(A) + N(B) - N(A \cap B) = 3 + 2 - 1 = 4.$$

As a final example, consider $A = \{a, b\}$ and $B = \{c, d\}$. Then $A \cup B = \{a, b, c, d\}$ and $N(A \cup B) = 4$. But now $N(A) = 2$, $N(B) = 2$, and, since $A \cap B = \varnothing$, $N(A \cap B) = 0$. Thus

$$N(A) + N(B) - N(A \cap B) = 2 + 2 - 0 = 4.$$

Our previous formula, $N(A \cup B) = N(A) + N(B) - N(A \cap B)$, can be generalized as

$$N(A \cup B \cup C) = N(A) + N(B) + N(C) - N(A \cap B)$$
$$- N(A \cap C) - N(B \cap C) + N(A \cap B \cap C)$$

and justified by a similar process of reasoning. For by $N(A \cup B \cup C)$ we mean the number of elements that are in A or in B or in C.* Thus we first count the number of elements in A, B, and C separately. Then we subtract the number of those we have counted twice because they are in both A and B. For similar reasons we subtract $N(A \cap C)$ and $N(B \cap C)$. Now, however, we may have subtracted twice because some elements may be in A, in B, and in C. Hence we add on $N(A \cap B \cap C)$.

A picture (*Venn* diagram) may help to clarify this procedure (Figure 19). Here the three sets A, B, and C are considered as the points

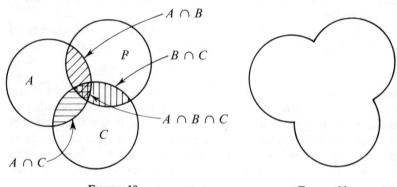

FIGURE 19   FIGURE 20

interior to the three circles A, B, and C; by $N(A)$, $N(B)$, and $N(C)$ we mean the respective areas of these three circles. To find $N(A \cup B \cup C)$ is to find the area shown in Figure 20. Our procedure is first to add together the areas of the three full circles to get $N(A) + N(B) + N(C)$. This obviously gives the areas of the shaded regions twice as shown in Figure 21. We thus subtract away these areas, $N(A \cap B)$, $N(A \cap C)$, and $N(B \cap C)$, but in so doing we find that we have first added the small area pictured in Figure 22 three times as we added the areas of the three circles. Then, however, we subtracted this area three times as indicated by the triple hatch marks. So, finally, we must add $N(A \cap B \cap C)$.

---

* As before we use "or" in the inclusive sense. That is, we include all of the possibilities that an element is in just one of A, B, and C; that it is in A and B but not C; A and C but not B; B and C but not A; or in A, B, and C.

FIGURE 21   FIGURE 22

Still another way to establish the validity of the formula for

$$N(A \cup B \cup C)$$

is as follows. We know that $B \cup C$ is a set. Let us call it D. Then $N(A \cup B \cup C) = N(A \cup D)$. By our first formula we have

(1) $N(A \cup B \cup C) = N(A \cup D) = N(A) + N(D) - N(A \cap D)$.

But $A \cap D = A \cap (B \cup C) = (A \cap B) \cup (A \cap C)$ by one of the distributive laws for sets.* Letting $A \cap B = E$ and $A \cap C = H$ we have

$$N(A \cap D) = N(E \cup H) = N(E) + N(H) - N(E \cap H).$$

Now $E \cap H = (A \cap B) \cap (A \cap C) = (A \cap A) \cap B \cap C = A \cap B \cap C$ by the properties of sets (as elements of a lattice) under intersection. Hence

(2) $N(A \cap D) = N(A \cap B) + N(A \cap C) - N(A \cap B \cap C)$.

Also

(3) $N(D) = N(B \cup C) = N(B) + N(C) - N(B \cap C)$.

Using (2) and (3) in (1) we have

$$\begin{aligned} N(A \cup B \cup C) = N(A) &+ [N(B) + N(C) - N(B \cap C)] - [N(A \cap B) \\ &+ N(A \cap C) - N(A \cap B \cap C)] \\ = N(A) &+ N(B) + N(C) - N(A \cap B) - N(A \cap C) \\ &- N(B \cap C) + N(A \cap B \cap C) \end{aligned}$$

as desired.

* See problem 6 of Exercise 15.

As an example, suppose that $A = \{a, b, d\}$, $B = \{a, b, c\}$, and $C = \{b, d\}$. Then

$$A \cup B \cup C = \{a, b, c, d\} \qquad A \cap C = \{b, d\}$$
$$A \cap B = \{a, b\} \qquad\qquad B \cap C = \{b\}$$
$$A \cap B \cap C = \{b\}$$

so that

$$N(A \cup B \cup C) = 4 \qquad N(A \cap B \cap C) = 1$$
$$N(A \cap B) = 2 \qquad\qquad N(A) = 3$$
$$N(A \cap C) = 2 \qquad\qquad N(B) = 3$$
$$N(B \cap C) = 1 \qquad\qquad N(C) = 2.$$

Thus $N(A \cup B \cup C) = 4$ and also

$$N(A) + N(B) + N(C) - N(A \cap B)$$
$$- N(A \cap C) - N(B \cap C) + N(A \cap B \cap C)$$
$$= 3 + 3 + 2 - 2 - 2 - 1 + 1 = 4.$$

As another example consider $A = \{a, b, c\}$, $B = \{a, c, d\}$, and $C = \{b\}$. Then

$$A \cup B \cup C = \{a, b, c, d\} \qquad A \cap C = \{b\}$$
$$A \cap B = \{a, c\} \qquad\qquad B \cap C = \varnothing$$
$$A \cap B \cap C = \varnothing.$$

Thus $N(A \cup B \cup C) = 4$ and

$$N(A) + N(B) + N(C) - N(A \cap B)$$
$$- N(A \cap C) - N(B \cap C) + N(A \cap B \cap C)$$
$$= 3 + 3 + 1 - 2 - 1 - 0 + 0 = 4.$$

EXERCISE 13

1. Check the validity of the formula for $N(A \cup B)$ for the following cases:

   (a) $A = \{a, b\}$, $B = \{a, c\}$;
   (b) $A = \{a, b, c, d\}$, $B = \{a, b, c\}$;
   (c) $A = \{a\}$, $B = \{a, b, c, d\}$;
   (d) $A = \{a, b, c\}$, $B = \{d\}$.

2. Check the validity of the formula for $N(A \cup B \cup C)$ for the following cases:

   (a) $A = \{a, b, c, d\}, \quad B = \{c, d\}, \quad C = \{a, e\}$;
   (b) $A = \{a, b\}, \quad B = \{c, d\}, \quad C = \{e\}$;
   (c) $A = \{a\}, \quad B = \{b\}, \quad C = \{a, c, d\}$;
   (d) $A = \{a, b, c, d\}, \quad B = \{c, d\}, \quad C = \{a, d\}$.

3. Derive a formula for $N(A \cup B \cup C \cup D)$.

*   *   *

The Case of the Delinquent Surveyor

Market surveys of all kinds are very popular these days. A thriving business is being done in surveying brand preferences, record sales, etc., with the results reported back to the person footing the bill. Surely this person sometimes wonders whether the survey was made in the field or made up in an armchair. In particular, consider the plight of Mr. R. E. K. Rourke, who has laid out cold, hard cash to have a survey made of the drinking preferences of 1000 persons. Specifically, the investigator is to determine how many persons like rum, how many like bourbon, and how many vodka. It is, of course, quite possible that some of the persons being interviewed will confess to a liking for all three, that some will like rum and vodka but not bourbon, that some will like vodka but not bourbon or rum, and so on. It is even conceivable, in fact, that some might like none, but such persons are to be ignored in our survey. In other words, the investigator is instructed to interview 1000 persons who like at least one of the alcoholic beverages listed.

Some days later and considerably the worse for wear* the investigator reports that:

815 like bourbon,   560 like both bourbon and rum,
719 like rum,   465 like both bourbon and vodka,
614 like vodka,   420 like both rum and vodka,
              300 like all three.

Now Mr. Rourke is most naturally suspicious that the interviews did not really take place and that the figures presented were spun out

* In order to minimize his chances of meeting unqualified persons, the investigator has been conducting his survey in bars.

of the investigator's imagination, aided and abetted by drinks bought with Mr. Rourke's cold, hard cash. So, Mr. Rourke lets:

A = set of all persons interviewed who like bourbon;
B = set of all persons interviewed who like rum;
C = set of all persons interviewed who like vodka.

Then

$A \cup B \cup C$ = set of all persons interviewed;
$A \cap B$ = set of all persons interviewed who like both bourbon and rum;
$A \cap C$ = set of all persons interviewed who like both bourbon and vodka;
$B \cap C$ = set of all persons interviewed who like both rum and vodka;
$A \cap B \cap C$ = set of all persons interviewed who like all three.

Furthermore, according to the investigator,

$$N(A \cup B \cup C) = 1000 \qquad N(A \cap B) = 560$$
$$N(A) = 815 \qquad N(A \cap C) = 465$$
$$N(B) = 719 \qquad N(B \cap C) = 420$$
$$N(C) = 614 \qquad N(A \cap B \cap C) = 300.$$

Hence, if the investigator is reliable, $N(A \cup B \cup C)$, or 1000, should be equal to

$$N(A) + N(B) + N(C) - N(A \cap B)$$
$$- N(A \cap C) - N(B \cap C) + N(A \cap B \cap C)$$

which is, however,

$$815 + 719 + 614 - 560 - 465 - 420 + 300 = 1003.$$

Thus the figures reported are not consistent and at least cast some doubt on the veracity of the investigator.*

EXERCISE 14

1. A market investigator reported that, of 1000 persons, 814 like root beer, 714 cola, 640 ginger ale, while 622 like both root beer and cola,

---

* He might, of course, have simply made an honest mistake in his tallies. On the other hand, the figures could check out and still be faked. Thus if the investigator had been lucky or shrewd enough (or had bought a copy of this book) he might have reported, for example, the figures given, except for $N(A \cap B \cap C) = 297$.

550 like both root beer and ginger ale, 600 like both cola and ginger ale, and only 530 like all three. None reported not liking any of the three. Test the results of the survey.

2. The following problem appeared in an actuarial examination: Certain data obtained from a study of a group of 1000 employees in a cotton mill as to their race, sex, and marital status were unofficially reported as follows: 525 colored lives; 312 male lives; 470 married lives; 42 colored males; 147 married colored; 86 married males; 25 married colored males. Test this classification to determine whether the numbers reported in the various groups are consistent.

3. (From Lewis Carroll). In a very hotly fought battle, at least 70 per cent of the combatants lost an eye, at least 75 per cent an ear, at least 80 per cent an arm, at least 85 per cent a leg. How many lost all four members?

*   *   *

The Algebra of Sets

We make one more application of the ideas presented here. For this we need just a little more machinery. First of all, we imagine that we have a sort of a super-set or universe, U, of which all other sets to be considered are subsets. For example, if the sets that we wish to consider are $A = \{a, b\}$, $B = \{a, c\}$, and $C = \{b, d\}$ we may consider U as $\{a, b, c, d\}$ or $\{a, b, c, d, e\}$, and so on. Suppose that we choose $U = \{a, b, c, d\}$. Then by A' (relative to this choice of U) we mean the set of elements that are in U but *not* in A. Thus in our example, $A' = \{c, d\}$, $B' = \{b, d\}$, and $C' = \{a, c\}$. On the other hand, if we choose $U = \{a, b, c, d, e\}$, then $A' = \{c, d, e\}$, $B' = \{b, d, e\}$, and $C' = \{a, c, e\}$. We call A' the *complement of A* (relative to U).

We note that, for any universal set U, we have $U' = \varnothing$ (the null or empty set) and $\varnothing' = U$. Furthermore, for any set X we have

$(X')' = X$. Thus, for example, if $U = \{a, b, c, d\}$,

$$(A')' = \{c, d\}' = \{a, b\} = A.$$

In Table 3, we list a number of identities for any collection A, B, C, ... of sets that are all subsets of some universal set U. (Note the parallelism between the identities listed in the right-hand column and those listed in the left hand column.)

Table 3

(1)	$A \cup A = A$	(1')	$A \cap A = A$
			(idempotent properties)
(2)	$A \cup B = B \cup A$	(2')	$A \cap B = B \cap A$
			(commutative properties)
(3)	$A \cup (B \cup C)$ $= (A \cup B) \cup C$	(3')	$A \cap (B \cap C)$ $= (A \cap B) \cap C$
			(associative properties)
(4)	$A \cup (B \cap C)$ $= (A \cup B) \cap (A \cup C)$	(4')	$A \cap (B \cup C)$ $= (A \cap B) \cup (A \cap C)$
			(distributive properties)
(5)	$A \cup \varnothing = A$	(5')	$A \cap U = A$
			(identity properties)
(6)	$A \cup A' = U$	(6')	$A \cap A' = \varnothing$
(7)	$U' = \varnothing$	(7')	$\varnothing' = U$
(8)	$U \cup A = U$	(8')	$\varnothing \cap A = \varnothing$
	(9) $(A')' = A$		

Some of these identities such as (1) and (1') we have seen before in our general discussion of lattices. Others, such as (6) and (6'), are quite obvious from the definitions of $\cup$, $\cap$, and $'$. In fact, the only ones that are not quite evident upon a moment's reflection are the two labeled (4) and (4').* To see, for example, that

$$A \cup (B \cap C) = (A \cup B) \cap (A \cup C)$$

we suppose that we have an element x in $A \cup (B \cap C)$. Then, writing $x \in A$ to mean that x is an element of A, we have

$$x \in A \quad \text{or} \quad x \in B \cap C.$$

* In fact, we have seen (p. 25) that these are not properties of *all* lattices.

Hence

$$x \in A \quad \text{or} \quad (x \in B \quad \text{and} \quad x \in C).$$

But then

$$(x \in A \quad \text{or} \quad x \in B) \quad \text{and} \quad (x \in A \quad \text{or} \quad x \in C).$$

Hence

$$(x \in A \cup B) \quad \text{and} \quad (x \in A \cup C)$$

so that $x \in (A \cup B) \cap (A \cup C)$. Thus every element of $A \cup (B \cap C)$ is an element of $(A \cup B) \cap (A \cup C)$.

Conversely, if $x \in (A \cup B) \cap (A \cup C)$, then

$$(x \in A \quad \text{or} \quad x \in B) \quad \text{and} \quad (x \in A \quad \text{or} \quad x \in C).$$

Hence

$$(x \in A) \quad \text{or} \quad (x \in B \quad \text{and} \quad x \in C)$$

whence

$$(x \in A) \quad \text{or} \quad x \in (B \cap C).$$

Thus $x \in A \cup (B \cap C)$.

We now have that every element of $(A \cup B) \cap (A \cup C)$ is an element of $A \cup (B \cap C)$ and, conversely, that every element of $A \cup (B \cap C)$ is an element of $(A \cup B) \cap (A \cup C)$. We conclude that $A \cup (B \cap C) = (A \cup B) \cap (A \cup C)$.

This type of argument, while straightforward, is somewhat involved. For this reason it may be desirable to again utilize Venn diagrams. Thus in Figure 23, we consider B to be the points in the circle shaded ///,

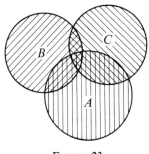

FIGURE 23

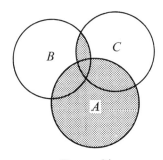

FIGURE 24

C to be the points in the circle shaded \\\, and A to be the points in the circle shaded |||. Then $B \cap C$ is the region shaded with both /// and \\\ and $A \cup (B \cap C)$ is the dark area shown in Figure 24. On the other hand, in Figure 25, $A \cup B$ is the portion of the figure shaded with horizontal lines and $A \cup C$ is the portion of the figure shaded with vertical lines. Then $(A \cup B) \cap (A \cup C)$ is the portion of Figure 25 shaded with both horizontal and vertical lines. Comparing this with Figure 24 we may feel reasonably confident of our assertion that

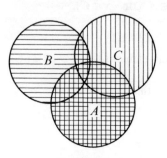

$$A \cup (B \cap C) = (A \cup B) \cap (A \cup C).$$

EXERCISE 15

1. If $U = \{a, b, c, d, e\}$, $A = \{a, b\}$, and $B = \{a, c, e\}$ find

(a) A' (d) $A' \cap B'$
(b) B' (e) $A' \cup B'$
(c) $(A \cap B)'$ (f) $(A \cup B)'$

FIGURE 25

2. Verify identity (4) in Table 3 for the following cases:

  (a) $A = \{a, b, c\}$, $B = \{a, b\}$, $C = \{a, c\}$.
  (b) $A = \{a\}$, $B = \{a, b, c, d\}$, $C = \{c, d\}$.

3. Verify identity (4′) for the two cases given in Problem 2.
4. Draw 2 Venn diagrams to illustrate the fact that $(A \cup B)' = A' \cap B'$.
5. Draw 2 Venn diagrams to illustrate the fact that $(A \cap B)' = A' \cup B'$.
6. Draw 2 Venn diagrams to illustrate identity (4′).

*   *   *

The Algebra of Switches

We are now going to apply this information about sets to the analysis of certain kinds of electrical circuits. For this we will need only the most elementary concepts concerning the flow of electricity. Thus we will consider circuits with switches in *series* (Figure 26) where, if any of the switches is open, no current will flow; and switches in *parallel* (Figure 27) where current will flow unless *all* of the switches are open. Furthermore we will combine switches in series and in parallel as shown in Figure 28. Here a and c are in series and, together, in parallel with b . Finally, if a circuit is so arranged that a switch c is always open

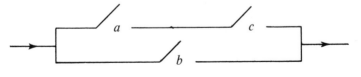

FIGURE 26

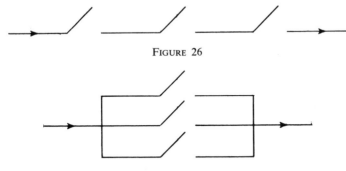

FIGURE 27

when another switch a is closed and, conversely, c is closed when a is open, we will designate c by a' .

FIGURE 28

Suppose now that Mr. Rourke, disgusted with the unreliability of surveys, has given up the idea of going into the liquor business and has become a manufacturer of Widgits. The device is immensely useful and would no doubt sell in huge quantities except for one slight flaw—it doesn't run. Mr. Rourke brings us a copy of the wiring diagram for the Widgit and it is as shown in Figure 29. After careful study of the situation we point out to him that one of the switches should be taken out. For, the labeling of the switches as a and a' indicates that if a is

FIGURE 29

closed then a' is open, and if a' is closed then a is open. Hence under no circumstances can the current flow.

Mr. Rourke takes our advice, has a switch removed, sells Widgits like mad, and recommends our services to Mr. N. Bourbaki, a manufacturer of Squidgits. Now Mr. Bourbaki has a problem too. It is rather the opposite of Mr. Rourke's in that the Squidgit cannot be turned off. The circuit diagram is brought to us and is as shown in Figure 30. Of course, it is again quite clear to us, if not to Mr. Bourbaki, what the trouble is. At all times either switch a is open or switch a' is open so that current can always flow along either the top half of the circuit or the bottom half. Once again a switch is removed and a manufacturer saved from ruin.

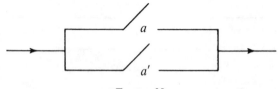

FIGURE 30

Our reputation is spreading. Now we are approached by Mr. J. L. Kelley, whose Handy Dandy Avocado Slicer works efficiently, can be turned on and off, but which, unfortunately, costs 33¢ more to make than his competitor's equally efficient product. The wiring diagram of the Handy Dandy Avocado Slicer is shown in Figure 31.

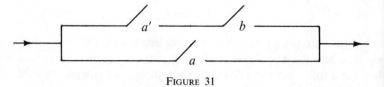

FIGURE 31

Now it seems plausible that the switch labeled a' might not really contribute anything to the circuit but this conclusion is by no means as obvious as were the conclusions in our previous examples. To see that we do not, indeed, need the switch a', we note that in this circuit we have the following possibilities:

$$\left.\begin{array}{ll} b & \text{open} \\ a & \text{open} \\ a' & \text{closed} \end{array}\right\} \quad \text{Current does not flow}$$

$$\left.\begin{array}{ll} b & \text{open} \\ a & \text{closed} \\ a' & \text{open} \end{array}\right\} \quad \text{Current flows (through bottom wire)}$$

$$\left.\begin{array}{ll} b & \text{closed} \\ a & \text{closed} \\ a' & \text{open} \end{array}\right\} \quad \text{Current flows (through bottom wire)}$$

$$\left.\begin{array}{ll} b & \text{closed} \\ a & \text{open} \\ a' & \text{closed} \end{array}\right\} \quad \text{Current flows (through top wire)}$$

Summarizing the results of our analysis: Current flows unless a and b are both open.

Now consider the circuit pictured in Figure 32. Clearly in this circuit, too, current flows unless a and b are both open. Thus the circuit

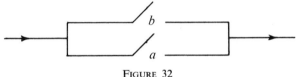

FIGURE 32

of Figure 32 does the same job as the circuit of Figure 31 and involves one less switch. Hence switch a' may be omitted and, since it costs 33¢, Mr. Kelley is back in the highly competitive avocado slicer market.

The analysis of the last circuit became slightly complicated. If we now consider the circuit shown in Figure 33 we might well decide that it would be worthwhile to investigate the possibility of a simpler way of analyzing circuits.

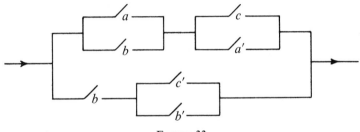

FIGURE 33

One way of doing this is to let circuits correspond to sets as follows:

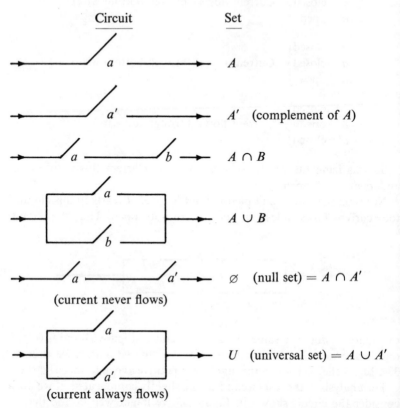

Then to any circuit is associated a set. The circuit of Figure 31 corresponds to $(A' \cap B) \cup A$ where $A' \cap B$ corresponds to the top part of the circuit. In Figure 33, the top part of the circuit corresponds to

$$(A \cup B) \cap (C \cup A')$$

and the bottom part to

$$B \cap (C' \cup B').$$

Thus the entire circuit corresponds to

$$[(A \cup B) \cap (C \cup A')] \cup [B \cap (C' \cup B')].$$

Now by means of the identities for sets (Table 3, page 36) we can always change the form of any expression involving sets. Thus, for example, $A \cap B = B \cap A$. For circuits this will then mean that the two circuits shown in Figure 34 are *equivalent* in the sense that for any combination of open and closed for the switches a and b in the circuit on the left which causes current to flow, the same arrangement

FIGURE 34

on the right will cause current to flow. A similar statement holds for the case when current does not flow. The specific combinations are listed below.

a	b	Current in left hand circuit	Current in right hand circuit
open	open	does not flow	does not flow
open	closed	does not flow	does not flow
closed	open	does not flow	does not flow
closed	closed	does flow	does flow

In this sense, too, we have seen that the circuits of Figure 31 and Figure 32 are equivalent since current does not flow in the circuit of Figure 31 only if a and b are both open and does not flow in the circuit of Figure 32 only if a and b are both open. Corresponding to the equivalence of the two circuits we have the set equality

$$(A' \cap B) \cup A = B \cup A$$

which is obtained as follows:

$(A' \cap B) \cup A = A \cup (A' \cap B)$	by (2) (commutativity of $\cup$);
$A \cup (A' \cap B) = (A \cup A') \cap (A \cup B)$	by (4) (distributivity of $\cup$);
$(A \cup A') \cap (A \cup B) = U \cap (A \cup B)$	by (6);
$U \cap (A \cup B) = (A \cup B) \cap U$	by (2');
$(A \cup B) \cap U = A \cup B$	by (5');
$A \cup B = B \cup A$	by (2).

Our general definition of equivalent circuits is as follows: Consider a circuit x in which some or all of the switches $\{a_1, a_2, \ldots, a_n\}$ are used (in series or in parallel) and another circuit y in which some or all of the switches $\{a_1, a_2, \ldots, a_n\}$ are also used (in series or in parallel). Then the circuit x will be said to be equivalent to the circuit y if any combination of open and closed for the switches $a_1, a_2, \ldots, a_n$ that causes current to flow in circuit x will also cause current to flow in circuit y. A similar statement, of course, must hold for the case when current does not flow.

From this and our definition of the correspondence between circuits and sets it should be reasonably clear that two circuits are equivalent if and only if the sets corresponding to the two circuits are equal. Thus since the two circuits of Figures 31 and 32 are equivalent we must have $(A' \cap B) \cup A = B \cup A$; and because we know from our discussion of sets that $(A' \cap B) \cup A = B \cup A$ we know that the two circuits of Figures 31 and 32 are equivalent.

Let us return to the circuit of Figure 33 to see if we can find, by the use of our algebra of sets, an equivalent and simpler circuit. We recall that our corresponding set is

(1) $[(A \cup B) \cap (C \cup A')] \cup [B \cap (C' \cup B')]$.

We transform (1) in the following steps:*

(2) $\{[(A \cup B) \cap C] \cup [(A \cup B) \cap A']\}$
        $\cup [(B \cap C') \cup (B \cap B')]$ [by (4') twice]
(3) $\{[(A \cup B) \cap C] \cup [A' \cap (A \cup B)]\}$
        $\cup [(B \cap C') \cup \varnothing]$ [by (2') and (6')]
(4) $\{[(A \cup B) \cap C] \cup [(A' \cap A) \cup (A' \cap B)]\}$
        $\cup (B \cap C')$ [by (4') and (5)]
(5) $\{[(A \cup B) \cap C] \cup [\varnothing \cup (A' \cap B)]\} \cup (B \cap C')$ [by (6')]
(6) $\{[(A \cup B) \cap C] \cup (A' \cap B)\} \cup (B \cap C')$ [by (2) and (5)]
(7) $[(A \cup B) \cap C] \cup \{(B \cap A') \cup (B \cap C')\}$ [by (2') and (3)]
(8) $[(A \cup B) \cap C] \cup \{B \cap (A' \cup C')\}$ [by (4')]

We now translate (8) back into a circuit as shown in Figure 35 and see that we have eliminated one switch and a little wire.

A considerable simplification can be made in such analyses by the following device. We replace $A \cup B$ by $A + B$, $A \cap B$ by AB

* A considerably simpler analysis will be given later and the analysis here may be skipped by the reader. In fact, the main purpose of including this first analysis is to show how matters may frequently be simplified by a change in notation.

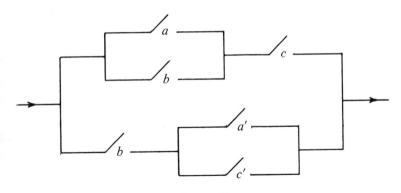

FIGURE 35

$\varnothing$ by 0 , and U by 1. Thus (1) becomes

(1') $(A + B)(C + A') + B(C' + B').$

Now our identities for sets tell us that we may operate as we do in algebra on such expressions as (1') using the ordinary laws of algebra and, in addition,

$$A + A' = 1, \qquad AA' = 0, \qquad 1 + A = 1,$$

$$(A \cup A' = U) \quad (A \cap A' = \varnothing) \quad (U \cup A = U)$$

$$A + A = \quad AA \quad = A,$$

$$(A \cup A = A \cap A = A)$$

and

$$A + BC = (A + B)(A + C)$$

$$[A \cup (B \cap C) = (A \cup B) \cap (A \cup C)].$$

Using this technique on (1') we obtain

(2') $AC + AA' + BC + BA' + BC' + BB'$
(3') $AC + 0 + BC + BA' + BC' + 0$
(4') $AC + BC + BA' + BC'$
(5') $(A + B)C + B(A' + C')$

The reader should check that (5') is the same as (8) in the new notation.

One of the problems in using this procedure is to determine whether or not further simplification of a circuit is possible. Thus, although (5') does represent a simpler circuit than (1'), we may go further by writing, in place of (5'),

(6') $AC + BA' + B(C + C')$
(7') $AC + BA' + B \cdot 1$
(8') $AC + BA' + B$
(9') $AC + B(A' + 1)$
(10') $AC + B \cdot 1$
(11') $AC + B = (A \cap C) \cup B$

Thus the circuit of Figure 33 is actually equivalent to the circuit of Figure 28.

We give one more example of this technique. Consider the circuit shown in Figure 36. Its corresponding set is

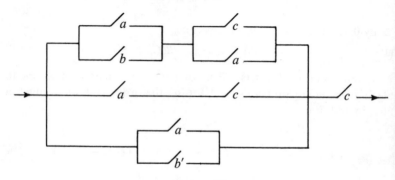

FIGURE 36

$$\{[(A \cup B) \cap (C \cup A)] \cap [(A \cap C) \cap (A \cup B')]\} \cap C,$$

or, in the simpler version,

$$(A + B)(C + A)(AC)(A + B')C.$$

Performing the algebra and using the fact that $A + A' = 1$, $AA' = 0$, $1 + A = 1$, $A + A = AA = A$ we have, in turn,

$$(A + B)(A + B')(A + C)(ACC)$$
$$(A + B)(A + B')(A + C)(AC)$$
$$(AA + AB' + BA + BB')(A + C)(AC)$$
$$(A + AB' + AB + 0)(AAC + ACC)$$
$$[A + A(B' + B)](AC + AC)$$
$$(A + A \cdot 1)(AC)$$
$$(A + A)(AC)$$
$$A(AC)$$

47

and finally,

$$(AA)C = AC = A \cap C.$$

Hence it follows that the circuit of Figure 36 is equivalent to the considerably simpler circuit of Figure 37.

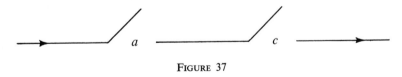

FIGURE 37

EXERCISE 16

Simplify, if possible, the following circuits by the use of the algebra of sets.

1.

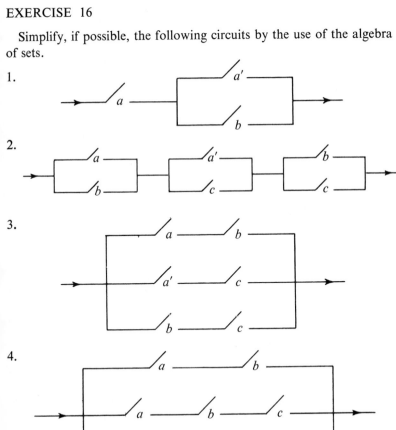

2.

3.

4.

5.

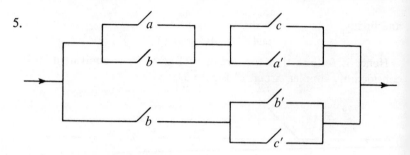

6.

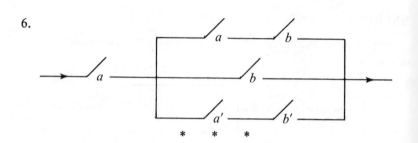

*   *   *

Convex Sets

We recall that we have defined a lattice as a partially ordered system in which every two elements have a least upper bound and a greatest lower bound. Nowhere did we say that the number of elements involved need be finite—although this was true of all of our examples to date. In our discussion of the number of elements in a set we used Venn diagrams in which our sets were considered as the points interior to circles—even though the sets actually under consideration were finite.

It is perfectly possible to consider in actuality (finite and infinite) sets of points in a plane and to define $\supseteq$, $\cup$, and $\cap$ exactly as was done for finite sets. Our universe, U, is simply the set of all points in the plane. The properties of finite sets listed on page 36 still hold and we do, in fact, have a (distributive) lattice. Since, however, this lattice has an infinite number of elements we do not have a diagram associated with it.

Figure 38 shows six examples of sets of points in a plane. In (a) we have pictured a set of three points; in (b) we have the set of points interior to a circle*; in (c) we have the points on a line segment; in (d) and (e) the points interior to irregularly shaped figures; and in (f) the points on a circle.

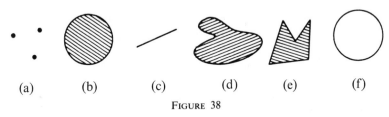

| (a) | (b) | (c) | (d) | (e) | (f) |

FIGURE 38

Let us now consider what are called *convex* sets in a plane. A convex set of points is a set of points A such that if $x \in A$ and $y \in A$, then every point on the line segment joining x and y is also in A. Thus (b) and (c) of Figure 38 picture convex sets but, as indicated in Figure 39, (a), (d), (e), and (f) do not as the point z is not in the given set.

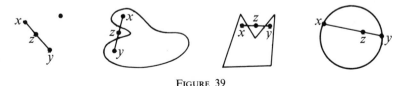

FIGURE 39

Let us now consider all of the convex sets in a plane. If A and B are convex sets we will give the same meaning to $A \supseteq B$ as before; that is, $A \supseteq B$ if and only if $x \in B$ implies $x \in A$. We will also interpret $A \cap B$ as before; that is, $x \in A \cap B$ if and only if $x \in A$ and $x \in B$. Note that if A and B are convex sets, then $A \cap B$ is a convex set. For if x and y are any two points in $A \cap B$, x and y are points of A and also points in B. Since A and B are convex

* It is, of course, not clear from the picture whether or not we are considering only the points interior to the circle or the interior points together with the points on the circle. Our convention will be that, unless otherwise stated, we are considering our pictures to represent only interior points.

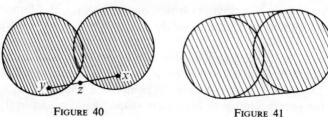

FIGURE 40   FIGURE 41

sets, the line segment joining x and y lies entirely in A and also entirely in B; hence it lies entirely in $A \cap B$ and $A \cap B$ is convex.

In general, however, as is shown in Figure 40, the union of two convex sets is not a convex set. So we define a slightly different kind of union,

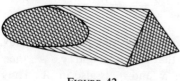

FIGURE 42

$A \vee B$, as the smallest *convex* set that contains both A and B (that is, $A \vee B$ is the least upper bound of A and B among the set of convex sets). For A and B as in Figure 40, $A \vee B$ is shown in Figure 41. In general, to form $A \vee B$ we consider $A \cup B$ together with

all the points on the line segments joining any point of A with any point of B. This is illustrated further in Figure 42.

Now, however, while the set of all convex sets with $\supseteq$, $\cap$, and $\vee$ defined as above do form a lattice, they do not form a distributive

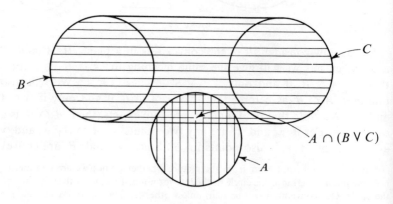

FIGURE 43

lattice. This is shown in Figure 43 where A, B, and C are the interiors of the three circles as shown; $B \vee C$ is the area shaded horizontally; and $A \cap (B \vee C)$ is the area shaded both horizontally and vertically. On the other hand, $A \cap B = \varnothing = A \cap C$ so that $(A \cap B) \vee (A \cap C) = \varnothing \vee \varnothing = \varnothing$. Thus

$$A \cap (B \vee C) \neq (A \cap B) \vee (A \cap C) .$$

The Algebra of Logic

We have seen that many seemingly different situations have very similar mathematical interpretations centering around the idea of a lattice. As a final example, let us consider some elementary logic. Here we are concerned with sentences—called statements—that are either true or false. Thus "Olympia is the capital of Washington" (true) and "Alaska is the smallest state in the United States" (false) are both statements; but "Please pass the cream" and "Where are you going?" are not statements.*

We will designate statements by the letters p, q, r, ..., and proceed to form new statements from given statements in the following ways:

(1) Negating a statement;
(2) Forming the conjunction of two statements; and
(3) Forming the disjunction of two statements.

For example, the statement "Olympia is the capital of Washington" has as its negation the statement "Olympia is not the capital of Washington." Given any statement p we write $\sim p$ for the statement that is the negation of p . It is clear that if p is a true statement then $\sim p$ is a false statement and that if p is a false statement then $\sim p$ is

---

* A sentence such as "There is life on Mars" is, of course, true or false, but we have no way (in 1963!) of deciding. We may admit such sentences as statements, however, with the thought in mind that there is an (undetermined) truth value.

a true statement. We may display this situation by means of a "truth table":

p	$\sim p$
T	F
F	T

The conjunction of two statements, p and q, is written $p \wedge q$ and is the statement that asserts p and q. Thus if p is the statement "Olympia is the capital of Washington" and q is the statement "Alaska is the smallest state in the United States," then $p \wedge q$ is the statement "Olympia is the capital of Washington and Alaska is the smallest state in the United States." If p and q are both true, then $p \wedge q$ is certainly true, but if either p or q (or both) are false, then $p \wedge q$ is false. Thus our truth table for $p \wedge q$ is as follows:

p	q	$p \wedge q$
T	T	T
T	F	F
F	T	F
F	F	F

and our example corresponds to the second line of the table.

Similarly, given two statements, p and q, we write $p \vee q$ for the statement that asserts p or q. Thus with p and q as in the preceding example, $p \vee q$ becomes the statement "Olympia is the capital of Washington or Alaska is the smallest state in the United States." Our truth table for $p \vee q$ is as follows:

p	q	$p \vee q$
T	T	T
T	F	T
F	T	T
F	F	F

This means that we agree to take $p \vee q$ as a true statement except when p and q are both false. (Our example corresponds to the second line of the table.) Notice in particular that our use of "or" demands that a statement such as "$2 + 2 = 4$ or $3 + 3 = 6$" be regarded as a true statement even though in ordinary discourse we would certainly say "$2 + 2 = 4$ *and* $3 + 3 = 6$." Also note that, in ordinary discourse, we usually demand some relationship between two statements connected by "or" as in "John went to the movies or John went to the ball game." Here, however, it would be perfectly in order to consider the statement "John went to the ball game or Olympia is the capital of Washington" (and this statement is a true statement regardless of whether or not John went to the ball game since it is true that Olympia is the capital of Washington).

The very use of the symbols "∧" and "∨" has undoubtedly led the reader to suspect that there is some connection between $p \wedge q$ for statements and $A \cap B$ for sets; between $p \vee q$ for statements and $A \cup B$ for sets; and between $\sim p$ for statements and A' for sets. Before we can make a precise statement of this connection, however, we need to define what we mean by *equivalent* statements. What do we mean, for example, when we write $p \wedge q \cong q \wedge p$? (Read "$p \wedge q$ is equivalent to $q \wedge p$"; compare $A \cap B = B \cap A$ for sets). Suppose that p and q are both true statements. Then $p \wedge q$ and $q \wedge p$ are both true statements. Similarly, if p is true and q is false, then $p \wedge q$ and $q \wedge p$ are both false. We summarize all possible cases in the following truth tables which may be condensed into one table:

p	q	$p \wedge q$
T	T	T
T	F	F
F	T	F
F	F	F

p	q	$q \wedge p$
T	T	T
T	F	F
F	T	F
F	F	F

p	q	$p \wedge q$	$q \wedge p$
T	T	T	T
T	F	F	F
F	T	F	F
F	F	F	F

Equivalence of $p \wedge q$ and $q \wedge p$, then, is established by the fact that the entries in the column headed $p \wedge q$ are the same as the entries in the column headed $q \wedge p$.

Similarly we establish that $\sim(\sim p) \cong p$ from the table

p	$\sim p$	$\sim(\sim p)$
T	F	T
F	T	F

since the entries in the column headed p are identical with the entries in the column headed $\sim(\sim p)$. (Compare $(A')' = A$ for sets.)

On the other hand, suppose that we wish to test whether or not $\sim(p \vee q) \cong (\sim p) \vee (\sim q)$. A table for this purpose is somewhat more complicated than the two previous ones we have used, so let us first consider the ideas behind its construction. Since two variables, p and q, are involved we will need to have four combinations of truth values for p and q (as in the table for $p \wedge q$ given previously). Suppose p is true and q is false. Now we need to calculate the truth value of $\sim(p \vee q)$ and of $(\sim p) \vee (\sim q)$. Since p is true, $p \vee q$ is true and thus $\sim(p \vee q)$ is false. This gives us the following portion of our table:

p	q	$p \vee q$	$\sim(p \vee q)$
T	F	T	F

Now we consider $(\sim p) \vee (\sim q)$. Since p is true and q is false, $\sim p$ is false and $\sim q$ is true. Thus $(\sim p) \vee (\sim q)$ is true. This gives us the following portion of our table:

p	q	$\sim p$	$\sim q$	$(\sim p) \vee (\sim q)$
T	F	F	T	T

Combining these two partial tables into one, we have

p	q	$p \vee q$	$\sim(p \vee q)$	$\sim p$	$\sim q$	$(\sim p) \vee (\sim q)$
T	F	T	F	F	T	T

This alone suffices to prove that $\sim(p \vee q) \not\cong (\sim p) \vee (\sim q)$ since, in the case when p is true and q is false, the entry for $\sim(p \vee q)$ is F and the entry for $(\sim p) \vee (\sim q)$ is T. Let us, however, look at the complete table as shown below. Notice that there are two cases where the

p	q	$p \vee q$	$\sim (p \vee q)$	$\sim p$	$\sim q$	$(\sim p) \vee (\sim q)$
T	T	T	F	F	F	F
T	F	T	F	F	T	T
F	T	T	F	T	F	T
F	F	F	T	T	T	T

truth value of $\sim(p \vee q)$ is the same as the truth value of $(\sim p) \vee (\sim q)$. These occur when p and q are both true so that $\sim(p \vee q)$ and $(\sim p) \vee (\sim q)$ are both false and when p and q are both false so that $\sim(p \vee q)$ and $(\sim p) \vee (\sim q)$ are both true. However, equivalence of $\sim(p \vee q)$ and $(\sim p) \vee (\sim q)$ means that the truth value of these two expressions must be the same for *all* possible truth values of p and q.

We apply this technique now to show that while

$$\sim (p \vee q) \not\cong (\sim p) \vee (\sim q)$$

we do have

$$\sim (p \vee q) \cong (\sim p) \wedge (\sim q) \quad .$$

(Compare $(A \cup B)' = A' \cap B'$ for sets.) The reader should check carefully the entries in each line of the table and observe the entries in the columns headed $\sim (p \vee q)$ and $(\sim p) \wedge (\sim q)$.

p	q	$p \vee q$	$\sim (p \vee q)$	$\sim p$	$\sim q$	$(\sim p) \wedge (\sim q)$
T	T	T	F	F	F	F
T	F	T	F	F	T	F
F	T	T	F	T	F	F
F	F	F	T	T	T	T

When more than two variables are involved, the procedure is the same except that there are more combinations of truth values possible. We illustrate this fact by proving that $p \wedge (q \vee r) \cong (p \wedge q) \vee (p \wedge r)$.

(Compare $A \cap (B \cup C) = (A \cap B) \cup (A \cap C)$ for sets.) Our table is as follows:

p	q	r	$q \vee r$	$p \wedge (q \vee r)$	$p \wedge q$	$p \wedge r$	$(p \wedge q) \vee (p \wedge r)$
T	T	T	T	T	T	T	T
T	T	F	T	T	T	F	T
T	F	T	T	T	F	T	T
T	F	F	F	F	F	F	F
F	T	T	T	F	F	F	F
F	T	F	T	F	F	F	F
F	F	T	T	F	F	F	F
F	F	F	F	F	F	F	F

Here we have eight rows corresponding to the eight possible combinations of truth values for p, q, and r. Consider, for example, the third line of the table. Here p is true, q is false, and r is true. Hence $q \vee r$ is true and thus $p \wedge (q \vee r)$ is true. Also $p \wedge q$ is false but since $p \wedge r$ is true, $(p \wedge q) \vee (p \wedge r)$ is true. We leave the check of the remaining lines to the reader and observe that since the entries in the column headed $p \wedge (q \vee r)$ are identical with the entries in the column headed $(p \wedge q) \vee (p \wedge r)$ we may conclude that $p \wedge (q \vee r) \cong (p \wedge q) \vee (p \wedge r)$.

We have now described what we mean by the equivalence of two statements and have, in fact, seen several parallels between logic and the algebra of sets that indicate the relationship between $\vee$ and $\cup$, $\wedge$ and $\cap$, and $\sim$ and $'$. For a complete parallel, however, we need logical equivalents to the universal set (U) and the null set $(\varnothing)$. For this purpose we consider the statements $p \vee (\sim p)$ and $p \wedge (\sim p)$ respectively. Their truth tables are shown below. From these we see that $p \vee (\sim p)$ always has the truth value T and $p \wedge (\sim p)$ always has the

p	$\sim p$	$p \vee (\sim p)$
T	F	T
F	T	T

p	$\sim p$	$p \wedge (\sim p)$
T	F	F
F	T	F

truth value F. Comparing these with $A \cup A' = U$ and $A \cap A' = \varnothing$ for sets, we write $p \vee (\sim p) \cong u$ and $p \wedge (\sim p) \cong \phi$.

We now note that $u \lor p \cong u$, $u \land p \cong p$, $\phi \lor p \cong p$, and $\phi \land p \cong \phi$ for any statement p. (Compare $U \cup A = U$, $U \cap A = A$, $\varnothing \cup A = A$, and $\varnothing \cap A = \varnothing$, respectively, for sets.) For u always has the truth value T and ϕ always has the truth value F and hence our truth tables for these equivalences are, respectively,

$u \lor p \cong u$			$u \land p \cong p$			$\phi \lor p \cong p$			$\phi \land p \cong \phi$		
u	p	$u \lor p$	u	p	$u \land p$	ϕ	p	$\phi \lor p$	ϕ	p	$\phi \land p$
T	T	T	T	T	T	F	T	T	F	T	F
T	F	T	T	F	F	F	F	F	F	F	F

It may be shown that every set identity involving $\cup$, $\cap$, and $'$ gives rise to a logical equivalence when we replace $\cup$ by $\lor$, $\cap$ by $\land$, $'$ by $\sim$, U by u, and $\varnothing$ by ϕ. (Whether we replace the conventional A, B, C, ... for sets by the conventional p, q, r, ... for statements is, of course, purely a matter of notation.) Conversely, every logical equivalence involving $\lor$, $\land$, and $\sim$ gives rise to a set identity when we replace $\lor$ by $\cup$, $\land$ by $\cap$, $\sim$ by $'$, u by U, and ϕ by $\varnothing$. We collect below the logical equivalences that we have established together with the corresponding identities of set algebra.

$p \lor q \cong q \lor p$ $A \cup B = B \cup A$
$\sim(\sim p) \cong p$ $(A')' = A$
$\sim(p \lor q) \cong (\sim p) \land (\sim q)$ $(A \cup B)' = A' \cap B'$
$p \land (q \lor r) \cong (p \land q) \lor (p \land r)$ $A \cap (B \cup C) = (A \cap B) \cup (A \cap C)$
$p \lor (\sim p) \cong u$ $A \cup A' = U$
$u \lor p \cong u$ $U \cup A = U$
$u \land p \cong p$ $U \cap A = A$
$p \land (\sim p) \cong \phi$ $A \cap A' = \varnothing$
$\phi \lor p \cong p$ $\varnothing \cup A = A$
$\phi \land p \cong \phi$ $\varnothing \cap A = \varnothing$

EXERCISE 17

1. Translate the following identities concerning sets into equivalences concerning statements:

(a) $A \cap B = B \cap A$
(b) $A \cap (B \cap C) = (A \cap B) \cap C$
(c) $A \cup (B \cap C) = (A \cup B) \cap (A \cup C)$
(d) $(A \cap B)' = A' \cup B'$

2. Translate the following equivalences concerning statements into identities concerning sets:

(a) $p \vee (q \vee r) \cong (p \vee q) \vee r$ (c) $\sim[(\sim p) \vee q] \cong p \wedge (\sim q)$
(b) $p \vee p \cong p$ (d) $p \vee (q \wedge r) \cong (p \vee q) \wedge (p \vee r)$

3. Construct truth tables for the following statements:

(a) $(\sim p) \vee q$ (c) $(p \vee q) \vee r$
(b) $p \vee (\sim q)$ (d) $[(\sim p) \wedge q] \vee r$

4. Use truth tables to prove or disprove the following logical equivalences:

(a) $p \vee p \cong p$ (d) $(p \vee q) \wedge r \cong p \vee (q \wedge r)$
(b) $p \vee q \cong (\sim q) \wedge (\sim p)$ (e) $p \vee (q \wedge r) \cong (p \vee q) \wedge (p \vee r)$
(c) $\sim[(\sim p) \vee q] \cong p \wedge (\sim q)$ (f) $p \vee (q \vee r) \cong (p \vee q) \vee r$

$$* \qquad * \qquad *$$

If we were to continue our parallel of logic with the algebra of sets we would want to define $p \geq q$ to correspond with $A \supseteq B$ for sets. In fact, we would conjecture that we would want to have $p \geq q$ if and only if $p \vee q \cong p$ since we have, from problem 2 of Exercise 12, $A \supseteq B$ if and only if $A \cup B = A$. It turns out, however, that such an interpretation of $p \geq q$ would not be of any significance in a discussion of logic.

It is true, however, that it is useful in logic to consider the combination of statements $(\sim p) \vee q$, and that $p \supset q$ (read "p implies q") is defined as being equivalent to $(\sim p) \vee q$. Thus the truth table for $p \supset q$ is as shown below (see problem 3a of Exercises 17):

p	q	$\sim p$	$(\sim p) \vee q \quad (\cong p \supset q)$
T	T	F	T
T	F	F	F
F	T	T	T
F	F	T	T

Hence we see that $p \supset q$ has the truth value T except when p is true and q is false.

EXERCISE 18

1. We may also read $p \supset q$ as "If p, then q." Consider the following statements:

   (a) If $2 + 2 = 4$, then $3 + 3 = 5$:
   (b) If $2 + 2 = 5$, then $3 + 3 = 5$;
   (c) If $2 + 2 = 5$, then $3 + 3 = 6$;
   (d) If $2 + 2 = 4$, then $3 + 3 = 6$.

   Which line of the preceding table for $p \supset q$ does statement (a) correspond to? Statement (b)? Statement (c)? Statement (d)? Hence which of the statements are true and which are false according to the agreed-upon conventions of the table?

2. Prove that $(p \supset q) \cong (q \supset p)$. (The statement $q \supset p$ is called the *converse* of the statement $p \supset q$.)

3. Prove that $(p \supset q) \cong ((\sim q) \supset (\sim p))$. (The statement $(\sim q) \supset (\sim p)$ is called the *contrapositive* of the statement $p \supset q$.)

4. Prove that $(p \supset p) \cong u$.

5. Prove that if $p \supset q$ and $q \supset p$, then $p \cong q$. That is, prove that if $p \supset q$ has the truth value T and $q \supset p$ has the truth value T, then p and q must have the same truth value.

6. Prove that if $p \supset q$ and $q \supset r$, then $p \supset r$. That is, prove that if $p \supset q$ has the truth value T and $q \supset r$ has the truth value T, then $p \supset r$ must have truth value T.

History and Suggestions for Further Reading

Basic to all of our discussion is the concept of $X \supseteq Y$ as used in our lattices and in our algebra of sets. We saw (pages 2–5) that we have (1) $A \supseteq A$; (2) if $A \supseteq B$ and $B \supseteq A$, then $A = B$; and (3) if $A \supseteq B$ and $B \supseteq C$, then $A \supseteq C$.* We remarked that a system in which there occurs a relation " $\supseteq$ " satisfying these three properties is called a partially ordered system and the consideration of such systems (in a somewhat unsystematic way) dates back to G. Leibniz (*ca.* 1690) who, with Isaac Newton, was a cofounder of the calculus. The first systematic discussions of such systems were made by C. S. Pierce in 1880 and E. Schroder in 1890 and the terminology was first introduced by F. Hausdorff in 1914 ("teilweise geordnete Menge" in German).

The idea of drawing diagrams to picture such orderings goes back at least as far as 1895 in a publication by H. Vogt, but such diagrams were first popularized somewhat later by H. Hasse and, as a consequence, they are commonly referred to as "Hasse diagrams."

To the concept of " $\supseteq$ " we added the notion of " $\cup$ " and " $\cap$ " which we defined in terms of " $\supseteq$ " as was first done by C. S. Pierce in 1880. During the next twenty years following Pierce's remarks there was little realization of the abundance of examples of lattices† in mathematics and R. Dedekind seems to have been the first to point out this abundance in 1900. Later, E. Noether stressed their importance in algebra and, still later, F. Klein, K. Menger, and G. Birkhoff pointed out their significance in other branches of mathematics.

A fundamental book on lattices is *Lattice Theory*, revised edition, by G. Birkhoff (American Mathematical Society Colloquium Publications,

---

* Although we saw (page 58) that the " $\supset$ " used in logic was not a strict analogy to the " $\supseteq$ " of set algebra, it is true that the three properties listed above are properties of the " $\supset$ " used in logic. (See problems 4 through 6 of Exercise 18.)

† Called "Dualgruppen" by R. Dedekind, "Verband" by F. Klein, and "structure" by O. Ore.

vol. 25, 1948). This is, however, a highly technical work intended for the research mathematician. The same author has also written an excellent article, "What is a lattice?" published in the *American Mathematical Monthly* (vol. 50, 1943, pp. 484–487) but this is still relatively technical. In fact, by the very nature of lattices as a unifying device, a discussion of them is bound to take one into rather deep mathematical waters. Hence it is only natural that there is a paucity of elementary discussions of the subject.

On the other hand, there are available many excellent and relatively elementary treatments of the algebra of sets and of symbolic logic. These subjects, of course, may be treated quite independently of lattices and the references given here contain little or no mention of the lattice viewpoint.

The primitive idea of a set, of course, goes back almost to the very beginnings of mathematics: a set of numbers, a set of points, and so forth. As a mathematical discipline in itself, the theory of sets originated with G. Cantor in 1870. Much of his work, however, was concerned with problems concerning infinite sets and these problems have been largely ignored in this book. The originator of the algebraic point of view of sets, together with their application to logic, was G. Boole in 1847. His *Investigation of the Laws of Thought* (reprinted in a paperback edition by Dover Publications, Inc., New York, 1951) is still very much worth-while reading and quite nontechnical. More modern and relatively nontechnical discussions of sets and logic are available in:

ANDREE, R. V., *Selections from Modern Abstract Algebra*. New York: Henry Holt & Co., 1958 (Chapter 3).

ARNOLD, B. H., *Logic and Boolean Algebra*. Englewood Cliffs, New Jersey: Prentice-Hall, Inc., 1962.

HOHN, F. E., *Applied Boolean Algebra*. New York: The Macmillan Company, 1960 (paperback).

KAMKE, E., *Theory of Sets*. New York: Dover Publications, Inc., 1950 (paperback).

STOLL, R. R., *Sets, Logic, and Axiomatic Theories*. San Francisco: W. H. Freeman & Co., Publishers, 1961 (paperback).

TARSKI, A., *Introduction to Logic and the Methodology of Deductive Science* (2d ed., revised). New York: Oxford University Press, Inc., 1954.

Answers to Exercises

Exercise 1

1. T
2. F
3. T
4. T
5. T

6. T
7. F
8. T
9. T
10. F

Exercise 2

1. (a) F
   (b) T
   (c) T
   (d) T

   (e) T
   (f) F
   (g) T
   (h) T

2. (a) T
   (b) T
   (c) F
   (d) F

   (e) F
   (f) F
   (g) T
   (h) F

3.

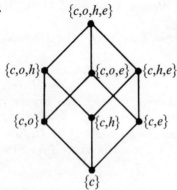

4.

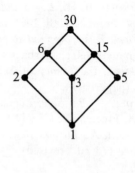

Exercise 3

1. w; $A \cup B = w$
2. p, w; $A \cup B = p$
3. o, w; $A \cup B = o$
4. b, g, p, w; $A \cup B = b$

5. w; $A \cup B = w$
6. r, o, p, w; $A \cup B = r$
7. w; $A \cup B = w$
8. k, y, b, r, g, o, p, w; $A \cup B = k$

Exercise 4

1. (a) y, k; $A \cap B = y$
   (b) k; $A \cap B = k$
   (c) r, k; $A \cap B = r$
   (d) k; $A \cap B = k$

   (e) g, y, b, k; $A \cap B = g$
   (f) r, k; $A \cap B = r$
   (g) p, b, r, k; $A \cap B = p$
   (h) k; $A \cap B = k$

2. Suppose that $A \cap B = G$ and also $A \cap B = G'$. Then G and G' are both lower bounds of A and B by (1). But, then, by (2), if $G = A \cap B$ we have $G \supseteq G'$ and also by (2), if $G' = A \cap B$ we have $G' \supseteq G$. We then apply the antisymmetric property to conclude that $G = G'$.

Exercise 5

1. $b \cup d = b$; $c \cup a = a$; $b \cap d = d$; $c \cap a = c$.
2. $a \cup c = a$; $d \cup e = d$; $a \cap c = c$; $d \cap e = e$.
3. $b \cup e = b$; $f \cup g = e$; $b \cap e = e$; $f \cap g = h$.
4. $b \cup a = a$; $c \cup d = a$; $b \cap a = b$; $c \cap d = e$.
5. (a), (b), (e), (f), (g), and (j) represent lattices; (c), (d), (h), and (i) do not represent lattices.

Exercise 6

1. (a) and (d).
2. (a), (b), and (d).

3.

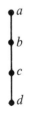

(b)

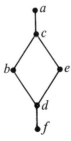

(e)

Exercise 7

These criteria apply to all of the diagrams of Figure 6, all of which are lattices; these criteria also indicate that (a), (e), (f), and (j) of the diagrams of problem 5 of Exercise 5 are lattices.

Exercise 8

There are not, of course, unique answers to these problems. Those given are only possibilities.

(a) We could take $a = 60$, $b = 30$, $c = 15$, $d = 5$, $e = 6$, and $f = 1$ and let $A \supseteq B$ mean, as before, that B divides A.

(b) As noted in the answer to problem 3 of Exercise 6, the lattice may be represented by

Hence the interpretation used for the lattice labeled (a) in Figure 6 may be used.

(c) As noted in the answer to problem 3 of Exercise 6, the lattice may be represented by

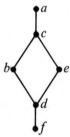

We may let $a = \{1, 2, 3, 4, 5\}$, $c = \{1, 2, 3, 4\}$, $b = \{1, 2, 3\}$, $e = \{1, 2, 4\}$, $d = \{1, 2\}$, and $f = \{1\}$ with $A \supseteq B$ if and only if every element of B is an element of A.

Exercise 9

1.

∪	a	b	c	d
a	a	a	a	a
b	a	b	b	b
c	a	b	c	c
d	a	b	c	d

2.

∪	a	b	c	d	e
a	a	a	a	a	a
b	a	b	b	a	b
c	a	b	c	a	c
d	a	a	a	d	d
e	a	b	c	d	e

3.

∪	a	b	c	d	e	f	g	h
a	a	a	a	a	a	a	a	a
b	a	b	a	b	b	b	b	b
c	a	a	c	c	c	c	c	c
d	a	b	c	d	d	d	d	d
e	a	b	c	d	e	e	e	e
f	a	b	c	d	e	f	e	f
g	a	b	c	d	e	e	g	g
h	a	b	c	d	e	f	g	h

4.

∪	a	b	c	d	e
a	a	a	a	a	a
b	a	b	a	a	b
c	a	a	c	a	c
d	a	a	a	d	d
e	a	b	c	d	e

5.

∪	a	b	c	d	e	f
a	a	a	a	a	a	a
b	a	b	b	b	b	b
c	a	b	c	c	b	c
d	a	b	c	d	b	d
e	a	b	b	b	e	e
f	a	b	c	d	e	f

6.

∪	a	b	c	d	e	f
a	a	a	a	a	a	a
b	a	b	c	b	c	b
c	a	c	c	c	c	c
d	a	b	c	d	e	d
e	a	c	c	e	e	e
f	a	b	c	d	e	f

Exercise 10

1.

∩	a	b	c	d
a	a	b	c	d
b	b	b	c	d
c	c	c	c	d
d	d	d	d	d

2.

∩	a	b	c	d	e
a	a	b	c	d	e
b	b	b	c	e	e
c	c	c	c	e	e
d	d	e	e	d	e
e	e	e	e	e	e

3.

∩	a	b	c	d	e	f	g	h
a	a	b	c	d	e	f	g	h
b	b	b	d	d	e	f	g	h
c	c	d	c	d	e	f	g	h
d	d	d	d	d	e	f	g	h
e	e	e	e	e	e	f	g	h
f	f	f	f	f	f	f	h	h
g	g	g	g	g	g	h	g	h
h	h	h	h	h	h	h	h	h

4.

∩	a	b	c	d	e
a	a	b	c	d	e
b	b	b	e	e	e
c	c	e	c	e	e
d	d	e	e	d	e
e	e	e	e	e	e

5.

∩	a	b	c	d	e	f
a	a	b	c	d	e	f
b	b	b	c	d	e	f
c	c	c	c	d	f	f
d	d	d	d	d	f	f
e	e	e	f	f	e	f
f	f	f	f	f	f	f

6.

∩	a	b	c	d	e	f
a	a	b	c	d	e	f
b	b	b	b	d	d	f
c	c	b	c	d	e	f
d	d	d	d	d	d	f
e	e	d	e	d	e	f
f	f	f	f	f	f	f

Exercise 11

1. (a) $a \cup (b \cup c) = a \cup b = a$; $(a \cup b) \cup c = a \cup c = a$.
   (b) $a \cap (b \cap c) = a \cap c = c$; $(a \cap b) \cap c = b \cap c = c$.
   (c) $a \cup (b \cap c) = a \cup c = a$; $(a \cup b) \cap (a \cup c) = a \cap a = a$.
   (d) $a \cap (b \cup c) = a \cap b = b$; $(a \cap b) \cup (a \cap c) = b \cup c = b$.

2. (a) $a \cup (b \cup d) = a \cup a = a$; $(a \cup b) \cup d = a \cup d = a$.
   (b) $a \cap (b \cap d) = a \cap e = e$; $(a \cap b) \cap d = b \cap d = e$.

3. (a) $b \cup (c \cup f) = b \cup c = a$; $(b \cup c) \cup f = a \cup f = a$.
   (b) $b \cap (c \cap f) = b \cap f = f$; $(b \cap c) \cap f = d \cap f = f$.
   (c) $b \cup (c \cap f) = b \cup f = b$; $(b \cup c) \cap (b \cup f) = a \cap b = b$.
   (d) $b \cap (c \cup f) = b \cap c = d$; $(b \cap c) \cup (b \cap f) = d \cup f = d$.

4. (a) $a \cup (c \cup d) = a \cup a = a$; $(a \cup c) \cup d = a \cup d = a$.
   (b) $a \cap (c \cap d) = a \cap e = e$; $(a \cap c) \cap d = c \cap d = e$.

5. (a) $a \cup (c \cup e) = a \cup b = a$; $(a \cup c) \cup e = a \cup e = a$.
   (b) $a \cap (c \cap e) = a \cap f = f$; $(a \cap c) \cap e = c \cap e = f$.

6. (a) $c \cup (b \cup d) = c \cup b = c$; $(c \cup b) \cup d = c \cup d = c$.
   (b) $c \cap (b \cap d) = c \cap d = d$; $(c \cap b) \cap d = b \cap d = d$.
   (c) $c \cup (b \cap d) = c \cup d = c$; $(c \cup b) \cap (c \cup d) = c \cap c = c$.
   (d) $c \cap (b \cup d) = c \cap b = b$; $(c \cap b) \cup (c \cap d) = b \cup d = b$.

7. An easy way to get the required examples is to take $A = B = C$. There are many other cases, however, where the distributive properties hold. For example, in the lattice labeled (b) we have

$$d \cup (b \cap c) = d \cup c = a, \quad d \cap (b \cup c) = d \cap b = e$$

and also

$$(d \cup b) \cap (d \cup c) = a \cap a = a, \quad (d \cap b) \cup (d \cap c) = e \cap e = e.$$

Similarly, in the lattice labeled (d) we have

$$a \cup (b \cap c) = a \cup e = a, \quad a \cap (b \cup c) = a \cap a = a$$

and also

$$(a \cup b) \cap (a \cup c) = a \cap a = a, \quad (a \cap b) \cup (a \cap c) = b \cup c = a.$$

8. We first remark (without proof) that every distributive lattice is modular but not conversely. In fact, it may be shown that the only lattices that are not modular are the one diagrammed as (b) in Figure 6 and lattices that contain such a lattice as a part [for example, (a) in Figure 16].

To show that the lattice labeled (b) is not a modular lattice we simply observe that $b \supseteq c$ but that

$$c \cup (d \cap b) = c \cup e = c$$

and

$$(c \cup d) \cap b = a \cap b = b.$$

To show that the lattice labeled (d) is indeed a modular lattice is a little more difficult since a large number of cases must be examined.

(a)   First suppose $C = e$. Then

$$A \cup (B \cap C) = (A \cup B) \cap C \qquad (1)$$

becomes

$$A \cup (B \cap e) = (A \cup B) \cap e$$

or

$$A \cup e = e.$$

But, since $C = e \supseteq A$, $A = e$ and $A \cup e = e \cup e = e$.

(b)   Next, suppose that $C = b$. Now $C \supseteq A$ means that $A = b$ or $A = e$. In the first case (1) becomes

$$b \cup (B \cap b) = (b \cup B) \cap b. \qquad (2)$$

Now if $B = a$ we have

$$b \cup (a \cap b) = (b \cup a) \cap b$$

and since $b \cup (a \cap b) = b \cup b = b$ and $(b \cup a) \cap b = a \cap b = b$ we have verified (1) for this case. If $B = b$, the result is obvious. If $B = c$, (2) becomes

$$b \cup (c \cap b) = (b \cup c) \cap b$$

and since $b \cup (c \cap b) = b \cup e = b$ and $(b \cup c) \cap b = a \cap b = b$ we have verified (1) for this case. The case $B = d$ is exactly similar to the case $B = c$. Finally, if $B = e$, (2) becomes

$$b \cup (e \cap b) = (b \cup e) \cap b$$

and since $b \cup (e \cap b) = b \cup e = b$ and $(b \cup e) \cap b = b \cap b = b$ we have verified (1) for this case.

(c)   The cases when $C = c$ or d are exactly similar to case (b).

(d)   Finally, suppose $C = a$. Then (1) becomes

$$A \cup (B \cap a) = (A \cup B) \cap a$$

or

$$A \cup B = A \cup B.$$

so that (1) is true in this case too.

Exercise 12

1. (a) $\{a, b, c\}$ (e) $\{a, b\}$
   (b) $\varnothing$ (f) $\{c, d\}$
   (c) $\{b, c, d, e\}$ (g) $\{a, b, c\}$
   (d) $\{e\}$ (h) $\{a, b\}$

2. If $X \cup Y = X$, every element of Y must be an element of X. That is, $X \supseteq Y$. Conversely, if $X \supseteq Y$, every element of Y is an element of X and hence $X \cup Y = X$.

3. If $X \cap Y = X$, then every element of X must be an element of Y. That is, $Y \supseteq X$. Conversely, if $Y \supseteq X$, every element of X is an element of Y and hence $X \cap Y = X$.

4. We first list all of the previously determined subsets of $\{a, b, c\}$. These are

$$\{a, b, c\} \qquad \{a, c\} \qquad \{a\} \qquad \{c\}$$
$$\{a, b\} \qquad \{b, c\} \qquad \{b\} \qquad \varnothing$$

Now, all of the sets just listed are also subsets of $U = \{a, b, c, d\}$ and the only other subsets of U are those that contain d. These are found by adding d to the list of elements in the sets above and are

$$\{a, b, c, d\} \qquad\qquad\qquad \{a, d\}$$
$$\{a, b, d\} \qquad\qquad\qquad \{b, d\}$$
$$\{a, c, d\} \qquad\qquad\qquad \{c, d\}$$
$$\{b, c, d\} \qquad\qquad\qquad \{d\}$$

Hence U has $8 + 8 = 16$ subsets.

5. If $U = \varnothing$ we have $2^0 = 1$ subsets; if $U = \{a\}$ we have $2^1 = 2$ subsets, U and $\varnothing$; if $U = \{a, b\}$ we have $2^2 = 4$ subsets, U, $\{a\}$, $\{b\}$, and $\varnothing$. Our example with $U = \{a, b, c\}$ shows that a set of three elements has $2^3 = 8$ subsets. It seems reasonable to conjecture that a set of n elements has 2^n subsets. A formal proof by induction may be easily developed along the following lines.

Suppose we have a set U with k elements and that there are 2^k subsets

$$U, B, C, \ldots, \varnothing$$

of U.

Now consider the set U^* whose elements are the elements of U together with the element a^*. What are the subsets of U^* ? First of all, they are the 2^k subsets of U we had previously (see the solution to problem 4)

$$U, B, C, \ldots, \varnothing$$

since any subset of U is surely a subset of U^*. Now, how can we form other subsets of U^* that are not subsets of U ? Clearly all such new subsets must contain a^* and are, in fact,

$$U \cup \{a^*\}, B \cup \{a^*\}, C \cup \{a^*\}, \ldots, \varnothing \cup \{a^*\}$$

so that we now have $2^k + 2^k = 2^k(1 + 1) = 2^k \cdot 2 = 2^{k+1}$ subsets of U^*. Thus from a set of three elements with 2^3 subsets we move to a set of four elements with 2^4 subsets, and so on.

6.

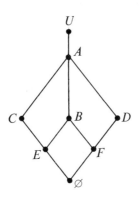

Exercise 13

1. We are to verify
$$N(A \cup B) = N(A) + N(B) - N(A \cap B).$$

(a) $A \cup B = \{a, b, c\}$, $A \cap B = \{a\}$
       $N(A \cup B) = 3$, $N(A) = 2$, $N(B) = 2$, $N(A \cap B) = 1$
       $3 = 2 + 2 - 1$.

(b) $A \cup B = \{a, b, c, d\}$, $A \cap B = \{a, b, c\}$
       $N(A \cup B) = 4$, $N(A) = 4$, $N(B) = 3$, $N(A \cap B) = 3$
       $4 = 4 + 3 - 3$.

(c) $A \cup B = \{a, b, c, d\}$, $A \cap B = \{a\}$
       $N(A \cup B) = 4$, $N(A) = 1$, $N(B) = 4$, $N(A \cap B) = 1$
       $4 = 1 + 4 - 1$.

(d) $A \cup B = \{a, b, c, d\}$, $A \cap B = \varnothing$
       $N(A \cup B) = 4$, $N(A) = 3$, $N(B) = 1$, $N(A \cap B) = 0$
       $4 = 3 + 1 - 0$.

2. We are to verify
$$N(A \cup B \cup C) = N(A) + N(B) + N(C) - N(A \cap B)$$
$$- N(A \cap C) - N(B \cap C) + N(A \cap B \cap C).$$

(a) $A \cup B \cup C = \{a, b, c, d, e\}$, $A \cap B = \{c, d\}$, $A \cap C = \{a\}$,
  $B \cap C = \varnothing$, $A \cap B \cap C = \varnothing$
$N(A \cup B \cup C) = 5$, $N(A) = 4$, $N(B) = 2$, $N(C) = 2$,
$N(A \cap B) = 2$, $N(A \cap C) = 1$, $N(B \cap C) = 0$, $N(A \cap B \cap C) = 0$.
  $5 = 4 + 2 + 2 - 2 - 1 - 0 + 0$.

(b) $A \cup B \cup C = \{a, b, c, d, e\}$, $A \cap B = \varnothing$, $A \cap C = \varnothing$,
  $B \cap C = \varnothing$, $A \cap B \cap C = \varnothing$
$N(A \cup B \cup C) = 5$, $N(A) = 2$, $N(B) = 2$, $N(C) = 1$, $N(A \cap B) = 0$,
$N(A \cap C) = 0$, $N(B \cap C) = 0$, $N(A \cap B \cap C) = 0$.
  $5 = 2 + 2 + 1 - 0 - 0 - 0 + 0$.

(c) $A \cup B \cup C = \{a, b, c, d\}$, $A \cap B = \varnothing$, $A \cap C = \{a\}$,
  $B \cap C = \varnothing$, $A \cap B \cap C = \varnothing$
$N(A \cup B \cup C) = 4$, $N(A) = 1$, $N(B) = 1$, $N(C) = 3$,
$N(A \cap B) = 0$, $N(A \cap C) = 1$, $N(B \cap C) = 0$, $N(A \cap B \cap C) = 0$.
  $4 = 1 + 1 + 3 - 0 - 1 - 0 + 0$.

(d) $A \cup B \cup C = \{a, b, c, d\}$, $A \cap B = \{c, d\}$, $A \cap C = \{a, d\}$,
  $B \cap C = \{d\}$, $A \cap B \cap C = \{d\}$.
$N(A \cup B \cup C) = 4$, $N(A) = 4$, $N(B) = 2$, $N(C) = 2$, $N(A \cap B) = 2$,
$N(A \cap C) = 2$, $N(B \cap C) = 1$, $N(A \cap B \cap C) = 1$.
  $4 = 4 + 2 + 2 - 2 - 2 - 1 + 1$.

3. We let $B \cup C \cup D = E$ and have

$$N(A \cup B \cup C \cup D) = N(A \cup E)$$
$$= N(A) + N(E) - N(A \cap E). \qquad (1)$$

By our previous result we have

$$N(E) = N(B \cup C \cup D) = N(B) + N(C) + N(D) - N(B \cap C)$$
$$- N(B \cap D) - N(C \cap D) + N(B \cap C \cap D). \qquad (2)$$

Now $A \cap E = A \cap (B \cup C \cup D)$
$$= (A \cap B) \cup (A \cap C) \cup (A \cap D).$$
We let $A \cap B = X$, $A \cap C = Y$, $A \cap D = Z$ and have

$$N(A \cap E) = N(X \cup Y \cup Z) = N(X) + N(Y) + N(Z)$$
$$- N(X \cap Y) - N(X \cap Z) - N(Y \cap Z)$$
$$+ N(X \cap Y \cap Z). \qquad (3)$$

But
$$X \cap Y = (A \cap B) \cap (A \cap C) = A \cap B \cap C,$$
$$X \cap Z = (A \cap B) \cap (A \cap D) = A \cap B \cap D,$$
$$Y \cap Z = (A \cap C) \cap (A \cap D) = A \cap C \cap D,$$
and $X \cap Y \cap Z = (A \cap B) \cap (A \cap C) \cap (A \cap D)$
$$= A \cap B \cap C \cap D.$$

Thus (3) becomes

$$N(A \cap E) = N(A \cap B) + N(A \cap C) + N(A \cap D)$$
$$- N(A \cap B \cap C) - N(A \cap B \cap D) - N(A \cap C \cap D)$$
$$+ N(A \cap B \cap C \cap D). \tag{4}$$

Using (2) and (4) in (1) we obtain

$$N(A \cup B \cup C \cup D) = N(A) + [N(B) + N(C) + N(D)$$
$$- N(B \cap C) - N(B \cap D) - N(C \cap D) + N(B \cap C \cap D)]$$
$$- [N(A \cap B) + N(A \cap C) + N(A \cap D) - N(A \cap B \cap C)$$
$$- N(A \cap B \cap D) - N(A \cap C \cap D) + N(A \cap B \cap C \cap D)]$$
$$= [N(A) + N(B) + N(C) + N(D)] - [N(A \cap B) + N(A \cap C)$$
$$+ N(A \cap D) + N(B \cap C) + N(B \cap D) + N(C \cap D)]$$
$$+ [N(A \cap B \cap C) + N(A \cap B \cap D) + N(A \cap C \cap D)$$
$$+ N(B \cap C \cap D)] - N(A \cap B \cap C \cap D).$$

Exercise 14

1. Let
$$A = \text{set of persons liking root beer};$$
$$N(A) = 814;$$
$$B = \text{set of persons liking cola};$$
$$N(B) = 714;$$
$$C = \text{set of persons liking ginger ale};$$
$$N(C) = 640;$$

Then $A \cap B = \text{set of persons liking both root beer and cola};$
$$N(A \cap B) = 622;$$
$$A \cap C = \text{set of persons liking both root beer and ginger ale};$$
$$N(A \cap C) = 550;$$
$$B \cap C = \text{set of persons liking both cola and ginger ale};$$
$$N(B \cap C) = 600;$$
$$A \cap B \cap C = \text{set of persons liking all three};$$
$$N(A \cap B \cap C) = 530.$$

Then we should have
$$1000 = 814 + 714 + 640 - 622 - 550 - 600 + 530.$$
But the sum on the right is equal to 926.

2. Let

$$A = \text{set of colored lives;}$$
$$N(A) = 525$$
$$B = \text{set of male lives;}$$
$$N(B) = 312$$
$$C = \text{set of married lives;}$$
$$N(C) = 470.$$

Then

$$A \cap B = \text{set of colored males;}$$
$$N(A \cap B) = 42$$
$$A \cap C = \text{set of married colored;}$$
$$N(A \cap C) = 147$$
$$B \cap C = \text{set of married males;}$$
$$N(B \cap C) = 86$$
$$A \cap B \cap C = \text{set of married colored males;}$$
$$N(A \cap B \cap C) = 25.$$

Thus

$$\begin{aligned}
N(A \cup B \cup C) &= N(A) + N(B) + N(C) - N(A \cap B) \\
&\quad - N(A \cap C) - N(B \cap C) + N(A \cap B \cap C) \\
&= 525 + 312 + 470 - 42 - 147 - 86 + 25 \\
&= 1057 \neq 1000
\end{aligned}$$

so that the numbers reported in the various groups are not consistent.

3. Let

$$A = \text{set of combatants who lost an eye;}$$
$$B = \text{set of combatants who lost an ear;}$$
$$C = \text{set of combatants who lost an arm;}$$
$$D = \text{set of combatants who lost a leg.}$$

We are interested in the number of combatants who lost all four members; that is, in $N(A \cap B \cap C \cap D)$. For simplicity, suppose there were 100 combatants. At least 85 of these lost a leg. Now consider the set of at least 80 who lost an arm. Since at most 15 did not lose a leg, at least $80 - 15 = 65$ lost an arm and leg. Thus at most $100 - 65 = 35$ did not lose both arm and leg and hence at least $75 - 35 = 40$ lost leg, arm, and ear. Thus at most $100 - 40 = 60$ did not lose leg, arm, and ear and hence at least $70 - 60 = 10$ lost all four members.

In general, by the same argument, we conclude that at least 10 per cent lost all four members and, of course, at most 70 per cent lost all four members.

Exercise 15

1. (a) $A' = \{c, d, e\}$
   (b) $B' = \{b, d\}$
   (c) $A \cap B = \{a\}$, $(A \cap B)' = \{b, c, d, e\}$
   (d) $A' \cap B' = \{d\}$
   (e) $A' \cup B' = \{b, c, d, e\}$
   (f) $A \cup B = \{a, b, c, e\}$, $(A \cup B)' = \{d\}$.

   [Note that, in this example, $(A \cap B)' = A' \cup B'$ and $(A \cup B)' = A' \cap B'$. (See problems 4 and 5.)]

2. Identity (4) is $A \cup (B \cap C) = (A \cup B) \cap (A \cup C)$.
   (a) We have $B \cap C = \{a\}$ and hence $A \cup (B \cap C) = \{a, b, c\}$.
        On the other hand, $A \cup B = \{a, b, c\}$ and $A \cup C = \{a, b, c\}$.
        Thus $(A \cup B) \cap (A \cup C) = \{a, b, c\} = A \cup (B \cap C)$.
   (b) We have $B \cap C = \{c, d\}$ and hence $A \cup (B \cap C) = \{a, c, d\}$.
        On the other hand, $A \cup B = \{a, b, c, d\}$ and $A \cup C = \{a, c, d\}$.
        Thus $(A \cup B) \cap (A \cup C) = \{a, c, d\} = A \cup (B \cap C)$.

3. Identity (4′) is $A \cap (B \cup C) = (A \cap B) \cup (A \cap C)$.
   (a) We have $B \cup C = \{a, b, c\}$ and hence $A \cap (B \cup C) = \{a, b, c\}$. On the other hand, $A \cap B = \{a, b\}$ and $A \cap C = \{a, c\}$. Thus $(A \cap B) \cup (A \cap C) = \{a, b, c\} = A \cap (B \cup C)$.
   (b) We have $B \cup C = \{a, b, c, d\}$ and hence $A \cap (B \cup C) = \{a\}$. On the other hand, $A \cap B = \{a\}$ and $A \cap C = \varnothing$. Thus $(A \cap B) \cup (A \cap C) = \{a\} = A \cap (B \cup C)$.

4.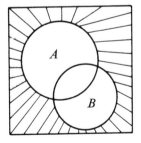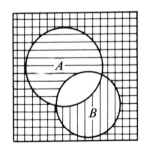

On the left, the shaded area represents $(A \cup B)'$. On the right, the area shaded horizontally represents B' and the area shaded vertically represents A'. Thus the area shaded both vertically and horizontally represents $A' \cup B'$.

5.

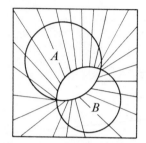   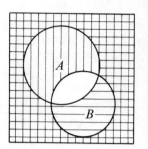

On the left, the shaded area represents $(A \cap B)'$. On the right, the area shaded horizontally represents A' and the area shaded vertically represents B'. The total area shaded either horizontally or vertically (or both) represents $A' \cup B'$.

6.

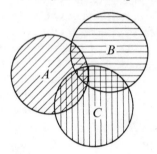

We shade A with ///, B with $\equiv$, and C with $\|\|$. Then $B \cup C$ is the region shaded either horizontally or vertically (or both) and $A \cap (B \cup C)$ is the region shaded slantwise and also horizontally or vertically.

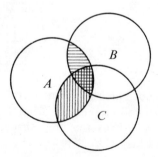

On the other hand, for $(A \cap B) \cup (A \cap C)$ we have shaded $A \cap B$ horizontally and $A \cap C$ vertically. Then $(A \cap B) \cup (A \cap C)$ is the region shaded either horizontally or vertically (or both).

Exercise 16

1. We translate our circuit as follows:

$$A \cap (A' \cup B) = A(A' + B).$$

Then

$$A(A' + B) = AA' + AB = 0 + AB = AB = A \cap B.$$

Translating back we have

2. We translate our circuit as follows:

$$(A \cup B) \cap (A' \cup C) \cap (B \cup C) = (A + B)(A' + C)(B + C).$$

Then

$$(A + B)(A' + C)(B + C) = (AA' + AC + BA' + BC)(B + C)$$
$$= (0 + AC + BA' + BC)(B + C)$$
$$= (AC + BA' + BC)(B + C)$$
$$= ACB + BBA' + BBC + ACC + BA'C + BCC$$
$$= ACB + BA' + BC + AC + BA'C + BC \quad (BB = B, CC = C)$$
$$= BC(A + A') + (BC + BC) + BA' + AC$$
$$= BC \cdot 1 + BC + BA' + AC \quad (BC + BC = BC)$$
$$= BC + BC + BA' + AC$$
$$= BC + BA' + AC$$
$$= (A + B)(A' + C) = (A \cup B) \cap (A' \cup C)$$

since $(A + B)(A' + C) = AA' + BA' + AC + BC = 0 + BA'$
$+ AC + BC = BA' + AC + BC.$

Translating back we have

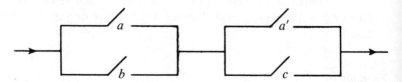

Note: This is the simplest answer. The original circuit had six switches and the one we finally obtained had only four. At any stage, however, we can translate our algebraic expression into an (electrically) equivalent circuit. At the second stage, when we obtained

$$(AA' + AC + BA' + BC)(B + C)$$

we would need ten switches. At the next to the last stage we had

$$BC + BA' + AC = (B \cap C) \cup (B \cap A') \cup (A \cap C),$$

which would translate into

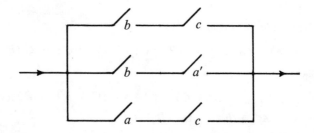

and would still necessitate six switches. Hence our clever (non-obvious) step at the end [where we wrote $BC + BA' + AC = (A + B)(A' + C)$] eliminated two switches.

3. Translating, we have

$$(A \cap B) \cup (A' \cap C) \cup (B \cap C) = AB + A'C + BC$$
$$= (A + C)(A' + B) = (A \cup C) \cap (A' \cup B)$$

since

$$(A + C)(A' + B) = AA' + A'C + BC + AB$$
$$= 0 + AB + A'C + BC = AB + A'C + BC.$$

Translating back we have

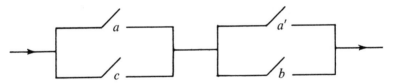

(Compare this with the last part of problem 2!)

4. Translating we have

$(A \cap B) \cup (A \cap B \cap C) \cup (A' \cap C)$
$= AB + ABC + A'C$
$= AB(1 + C) + A'C$
$= AB \cdot 1 + A'C$ (using $1 + C = 1$)
$= AB + A'C = (A \cap B) \cup (A' \cap C)$.

Translating back we have

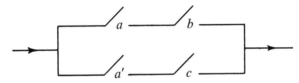

5. We translate our circuit as follows:

$[(A \cup B) \cap (C \cup A')] \cup [B \cap (B' \cup C')]$
$= (A + B)(C + A') + B(B' + C')$
$= AC + AA' + BC + BA' + BB' + BC'$
$= AC + 0 + BC + BA' + 0 + BC'$
$= AC + BC + BA' + BC'$
$= AC + B(C + C' + A')$
$= AC + B(1 + A')$
$= AC + B \cdot 1$
$= AC + B = (A \cap C) \cup B$.

Translating back we have

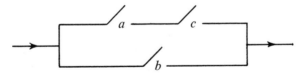

6. We translate our circuit as follows:

$$A \cap [(A \cap B) \cup B \cup (A' \cap B')]$$
$$= A(AB + B + A'B')$$
$$= (AA)B + AB + (AA')B$$
$$= (AB + AB) + 0 \cdot B$$
$$= AB + 0$$
$$= AB = A \cap B.$$

Translating back we have

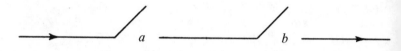

Exercise 17

1. (a) $p \wedge q \cong q \wedge p$ (c) $p \vee (q \wedge r) \cong (p \vee q) \wedge (p \vee r)$
   (b) $p \wedge (q \wedge r) \cong (p \wedge q) \wedge r$ (d) $\sim(p \wedge q) \cong (\sim p) \vee (\sim q)$

2. (a) $A \cup (B \cup C) = (A \cup B) \cup C$
   (b) $A \cup A = A$
   (c) $(A' \cup B)' = A \cap B'$
   (d) $A \cup (B \cap C) = (A \cup B) \cap (A \cup C)$

3. (a)

p	q	$\sim p$	$(\sim p) \vee q$
T	T	F	T
T	F	F	F
F	T	T	T
F	F	T	T

   (b)

p	q	$\sim q$	$p \vee (\sim q)$
T	T	F	T
T	F	T	T
F	T	F	F
F	F	T	T

(c)

p	q	r	$p \lor q$	$(p \lor q) \lor r$
T	T	T	T	T
T	T	F	T	T
T	F	T	T	T
T	F	F	T	T
F	T	T	T	T
F	T	F	T	T
F	F	T	F	T
F	F	F	F	F

(d)

p	q	r	$\sim p$	$(\sim p) \land q$	$[(\sim p) \land q] \lor r$
T	T	T	F	F	T
T	T	F	F	F	F
T	F	T	F	F	T
T	F	F	F	F	F
F	T	T	T	T	T
F	T	F	T	T	T
F	F	T	T	F	T
F	F	F	T	F	F

4. We construct complete truth tables for every problem even though only one line is needed to show inequivalence.

(a)

p	$p \lor p$
T	T
F	F

Hence $p \lor p \cong p$

(b)

p	q	$p \lor q$	$\sim q$	$\sim p$	$(\sim q) \land (\sim p)$
T	T	T	F	F	F
T	F	T	T	F	F
F	T	T	F	T	F
F	F	F	T	T	T

Hence $p \lor q \not\cong (\sim q) \land (\sim p)$. (Any one of the lines in our table would suffice to show this.)

(c)

p	q	$\sim p$	$(\sim p) \vee q$	$\sim[(\sim p) \vee q]$	$\sim q$	$p \wedge (\sim q)$
T	T	F	T	F	F	F
T	F	F	F	T	T	T
F	T	T	T	F	F	F
F	F	T	T	F	T	F

Hence $\sim[(\sim p) \vee q] \cong p \wedge (\sim q)$.

(d)

p	q	r	$p \vee q$	$(p \vee q) \wedge r$	$q \wedge r$	$p \vee (q \wedge r)$
T	T	T	T	T	T	T
T	T	F	T	F	F	T
T	F	T	T	T	F	T
T	F	F	T	F	F	T
F	T	T	T	T	T	T
F	T	F	T	F	F	F
F	F	T	F	F	F	F
F	F	F	F	F	F	F

Hence $(p \vee q) \wedge r \not\cong p \vee (q \wedge r)$. (Either one of lines 2 or 4 would suffice to show this.)

(e)

p	q	r	$q \wedge r$	$p \vee (q \wedge r)$	$p \vee q$	$p \vee r$	$(p \vee q) \wedge (p \vee r)$
T	T	T	T	T	T	T	T
T	T	F	F	T	T	T	T
T	F	T	F	T	T	T	T
T	F	F	F	T	T	T	T
F	T	T	T	T	T	T	T
F	T	F	F	F	T	F	F
F	F	T	F	F	F	T	F
F	F	F	F	F	F	F	F

Hence $p \vee (q \wedge r) \cong (p \vee q) \wedge (p \vee r)$.

(f)

p	q	r	$q \vee r$	$p \vee (q \vee r)$	$p \vee q$	$(p \vee q) \vee r$
T	T	T	T	T	T	T
T	T	F	T	T	T	T
T	F	T	T	T	T	T
T	F	F	F	T	T	T
F	T	T	T	T	T	T
F	T	F	T	T	T	T
F	F	T	T	T	F	T
F	F	F	F	F	F	F

Hence $p \vee (q \vee r) \cong (p \vee q) \vee r$.

Exercise 18

1. (a) Since $2 + 2 = 4$ is true and $3 + 3 = 5$ is false we have the pattern

p	q
T	F

Hence, by line 2 of the truth table for $p \supset q$, (a) is a false statement.
(b) Since $2 + 2 = 5$ is false and $3 + 3 = 5$ is false we have the pattern

p	q
F	F

Hence, by line 4 of the truth table for $p \supset q$, (b) is a true statement.
(c) Since $2 + 2 = 5$ is false and $3 + 3 = 6$ is true we have the pattern

p	q
F	T

Hence, by line 3 of the truth table for $p \supset q$, (c) is a true statement.
(d) Since $2 + 2 = 4$ is true and $3 + 3 = 6$ is true we have the pattern

p	q
T	T

Hence, by line 1 of the truth table for $p \supset q$, (d) is a true statement.

Discussion: In our discussion of $p \vee q$ (page 53), I pointed out that our formal definition of $p \vee q$ led us to the necessity of accepting such statements as " $2 + 2 = 4$ or $3 + 3 = 6$" and "John went to the movies or Olympia is the capital of Washington" as true. Implication as used in formal logic poses similar difficulties. If I say that "If . . . then $3 + 3 = 6$" we agree that it matters not what comes after the word "if" and before the word "then." The only thing that matters is that "$3 + 3 = 6$" is a true statement. This is why we say that statements like (c) and (d) are true. Now in ordinary discourse, it is true, we demand some relationship between what comes after "if" and before "then" (the *antecedent*) and what comes after "then" (the *consequent*), and if someone said "If $2 + 2 = 5$, then $3 + 3 = 6$" we would certainly say that the conclusion is correct but that the argument used in arriving at the conclusion is faulty (since $2 + 2 \neq 5$). It is not possible in formal logic, however, to insist upon such connections between antecedent and consequent.

Similarly, no matter how correct the antecedent might be (as $2 + 2 = 4$) we cannot be allowed to draw an incorrect result (as $3 + 3 = 5$). Thus we regard (a) as a false statement. This still leaves the most puzzling case of all. Why should (b) be regarded as a correct statement? Perhaps the most vivid way to look at this is through the old saying "If wishes were fishes, beggars would be kings" which, in some sense, is certainly a true statement. That is, granted the unlikely antecedent, the unlikely consequent follows or, more generally, the acceptance of any false statement implies the acceptance of every other false statement.

We shall not pursue these rather subtle questions further but simply assert that the use of implication in the way described here does lead to consistent and sensible results when applied to mathematics and the sciences. For further details the reader should consult the books on logic listed in the bibliography.

2.

p	q	$p \supset q$	$q \supset p$
T	T	T	T
T	F	F	T
F	T	T	F
F	F	T	T

Hence by either the second or third line of the table we conclude that $(p \supset q) \not\equiv (q \supset p)$.

3.

p	q	$p \supset q$	$\sim q$	$\sim p$	$(\sim q) \supset (\sim p)$
T	T	T	F	F	T
T	F	F	T	F	F
F	T	T	F	T	T
F	F	T	T	T	T

Hence $(p \supset q) \cong [(\sim q) \supset (\sim p)]$.

4.

u	p	$p \supset p$
T	T	T
T	F	T

Hence $(p \supset p) \cong u$.

5. We saw in problem 2 that we do not have $(p \supset q) \cong (q \supset p)$. Our truth table that showed this was as follows:

p	q	$p \supset q$	$q \supset p$
T	T	T	T
T	F	F	T
F	T	T	F
F	F	T	T

Hence if $p \supset q$ and $q \supset p$ are both true, it follows that either p and q are both true or p and q are both false. That is, when $p \supset q$ and $q \supset p$ arc both true, the truth table for p and q is as follows:

p	q
T	T
F	F

Thus if $p \supset q$ and $q \supset p$, p and q have the same truth table so that $p \cong q$.

6. Consider the truth tables for $p \supset q$ and $q \supset r$:

p	q	$p \supset q$
T	T	T
T	F	F
F	T	T
F	F	T

q	r	$q \supset r$
T	T	T
T	F	F
F	T	T
F	F	T

If $p \supset q$ and $q \supset r$ both have the truth value T , then we *cannot* have p true and q false or q true and r false. Consider now the truth table for $p \supset r$.

p	r	$p \supset r$
T	T	T
T	F	F
F	T	T
F	F	T

We are trying to show that the second line of the table cannot occur under the hypothesis that $p \supset q$ and $q \supset r$. Now the second line says that p is true. Hence q must be true since we have seen that we cannot have p true and q false. But if q is true we have seen that r cannot be false. Thus the second line of our table is indeed impossible and $p \supset r$ always has the truth value T.

Index

Algebra
    of logic 51–59
    of sets 35–38
    of switches 38–47
Antisymmetric property 2, 5
Associative property
    of lattices 23
    of sets 36
Avocado Slicer, Handy Dandy 40

Bourbaki, N. 40

Commutative property
    of lattices 23
    of sets 36
Complement of a set 35
Conjunction of statements 51–52
Connected points 9
Contrapositive 59
Converse 59
Convex sets 48–51
Counting 29–34

Disjunction of statements 51–52
Distributive property
    of lattices 24
    of sets 36

Empty set 27
Equivalent statements 53–54

Greatest lower bound 7

Idempotent properties
    of lattices 23
    of sets 36
Identity
    for lattices 23
    for sets 36
Intersection (or Meet)
    identity for 23
    in lattices 22
    of sets 27

Join (see Union)

Kelley, J. L. 40

Lattice
    of arithmetic student 3
    of colors 1
    of cook 3
    condition that a diagram represent
        9–11, 15
    definition of 8–9
    interpretations of 19–20
    modular 26
    properties of 23
    of subsets 28
Least upper bound 5
Logic, algebra of 51–59
Lower bound 7

Meet (see Intersection)

Negation of statements 51
Null set 27

Painting, lecturer on 1
Partially ordered system 5

Reflexive property 2, 5
Rourke, R. E. K. 33–34, 39

Sets
    algebra of 35–38
    complement of 35
    convex 48–51
    empty 27
    null 27
    universal 35
Squidgits 40
Statements
    conjunction of 51–52
    contrapositive 59
    converse of 59
    definition of 51
    disjunction of 51–52

88

Statements (continued)
    equivalent 53–54
    negation of 51
Subsets 27
Surveyor, delinquent 33–34
Switches
    algebra of 38–47
    in parallel 39
    in series 38–39

Transitive property 2, 5

Union (or Join)
    identity for 23
    in lattices 21
    of sets 27
Universal set 35
Upper bound 5

Venn diagram 30

Widgits 39

PRINTED IN THE UNITED STATES OF AMERICA

MA